Editor
Eric Migliaccio

Editor in Chief
Karen J. Goldfluss, M.S. Ed.

Cover Artist
Barb Lorseyedi

Illustrator
Clint McKnight

Art Coordinator
Renée Mc Elwee

Imaging
James Edward Grace

Publisher

Mary D. Smith, M.S. Ed.

Author
Heather Wolpert-Gawron

For information about Common Core State Standards, see pages 4–5 of this book or visit *http://www.teachercreated.com/standards*

Teacher Created Resources
6421 Industry Way
Westminster, CA 92683
www.teachercreated.com
ISBN: 978-1-4206-2783-1
© 2014 Teacher Created Resources
Made in U.S.A.

Table of Contents

Table of Contents *(cont.)*

Common Core State Standards

Project-Based Writing, Grade 5 gives students and teachers the necessary resources and ideas needed to create project-based-writing units in the classroom. During each step of this process, students will engage in activities that meet one or more of the following Common Core State Standards. (©Copyright 2010. National Governors Association Center for Best Practices and Council of Chief State School Officers. All rights reserved.) For more information about the Common Core State Standards, go to *http://www.corestandards.org/* or *http://www.teachercreated.com/standards/*.

Informational Text Standards

Key Ideas and Details

ELA.RI.5.1. Quote accurately from a text when explaining what the text says explicitly and when drawing inferences from the text.

ELA.RI.5.2. Determine two or more main ideas of a text and explain how they are supported by key details; summarize the text.

ELA.RI.5.3. Explain the relationships or interactions between two or more individuals, events, ideas, or concepts in a historical, scientific, or technical text based on specific information in the text.

Craft and Structure

ELA.RI.5.4. Determine the meaning of general academic and domain-specific words and phrases in a text relevant to a *grade 5 topic or subject area*.

ELA.RI.5.5. Compare and contrast the overall structure (e.g., chronology, comparison, cause/effect, problem/solution) of events, ideas, concepts, or information in two or more texts.

ELA.RI.5.6. Analyze multiple accounts of the same event or topic, noting important similarities and differences in the point of view they represent.

Integration of Knowledge and Ideas

ELA.RI.5.7. Draw on information from multiple print or digital sources, demonstrating the ability to locate an answer to a question quickly or to solve a problem efficiently.

ELA.RI.5.8. Explain how an author uses reasons and evidence to support particular points in a text, identifying which reasons and evidence support which point(s).

ELA.RI.5.9. Integrate information from several texts on the same topic in order to write or speak about the subject knowledgeably.

Range of Reading and Level of Text Complexity

ELA.RI.5.10. By the end of the year, read and comprehend informational texts, including history/social studies, science, and technical texts, at the high end of the grades 4–5 text complexity band independently and proficiently.

Writing Standards

Text Types and Purposes

ELA.W.5.1. Write opinion pieces on topics or texts, supporting a point of view with reasons and information.

ELA.W.5.2. Write informative/explanatory texts to examine a topic and convey ideas and information clearly.

ELA.W.5.3. Write narratives to develop real or imagined experiences or events using effective technique, descriptive details, and clear event sequences.

Common Core State Standards *(cont.)*

Writing Standards *(cont.)*

Production and Distribution of Writing

ELA.W.5.4. Produce clear and coherent writing in which the development and organization are appropriate to task, purpose, and audience.

ELA.W.5.5. With guidance and support from peers and adults, develop and strengthen writing as needed by planning, revising, editing, rewriting, or trying a new approach.

ELA.W.5.6. With some guidance and support from adults, use technology, including the Internet, to produce and publish writing as well as to interact and collaborate with others; demonstrate sufficient command of keyboarding skills to type a minimum of two pages in a single sitting.

Research to Build and Present Knowledge

ELA.W.5.7. Conduct short research projects that use several sources to build knowledge through investigation of different aspects of a topic.

ELA.W.5.8. Recall relevant information from experiences or gather relevant information from print and digital sources; summarize or paraphrase information in notes and finished work, and provide a list of sources.

ELA.W.5.9. Draw evidence from literary or informational texts to support analysis, reflection, and research.

Range of Writing

ELA.W.5.10. Write routinely over extended time frames (time for research, reflection, and revision) and shorter time frames (a single sitting or a day or two) for a range of discipline-specific tasks, purposes, and audiences.

Speaking and Listening Standards

Comprehension and Collaboration

ELA.SL.5.1. Engage effectively in a range of collaborative discussions (one-on-one, in groups, and teacher-led) with diverse partners on *grade 5 topics and texts*, building on others' ideas and expressing their own clearly.

Presentation of Knowledge and Ideas

ELA.SL.5.4. Report on a topic or text or present an opinion, sequencing ideas logically and using appropriate facts and relevant, descriptive details to support main ideas or themes; speak clearly at an understandable pace.

ELA.SL.5.5. Include multimedia components (e.g., graphics, sound) and visual displays in presentations when appropriate to enhance the development of main ideas or themes.

ELA.SL.5.6. Adapt speech to a variety of contexts and tasks, using formal English when appropriate to task and situation.

Foundational Skills Standards

Phonics and Word Recognition

ELA.RF.5.3. Know and apply grade-level phonics and word-analysis skills in decoding words.

Fluency

ELA.RF.5.4. Read with sufficient accuracy and fluency to support comprehension.

Introduction:
Nothing Fits in a Box Anymore

This book and the concepts contained within it are a direct response to the growing trend toward differentiation and individualization. The multi-genre, hybrid approach of *Project-Based Writing* recognizes the differences between students, how they learn, and how they seek to show their learning. It caters to their individual strengths, while also guiding them toward the exploration of other means of expression that they might instinctively tend to avoid.

Ultimately, project-based writing is about choice. Just as we live in a culture in which every person in the coffee line can have his or her own personalized beverage made to order, so, too, should students be given the tools and the opportunity to show off their knowledge in many different ways.

A vital aspect of project-based writing is the blending of school life with real life. Often, there is a disconnect between the two. Many students, especially tweens and teens, see school life as totally separate from life outside of school. Therefore, it becomes our job as teachers to make sure that the classroom more directly correlates to the outside world. Choice is a huge part of doing that. So whenever possible in your curriculum, you should feel encouraged to offer student choice, while of course still emphasizing academic rigor and content knowledge.

The multi-genre activities and units covered in *Project-Based Writing* offer the best of both worlds: students gain a functional knowledge of a whole slew of genres, formats, and ways of expressing themselves; and at the same time, they learn to successfully weave these separate elements together into a cohesive whole that digs deeper into the topics, themes, and issues that are most important to their lives outside of school. It is this step of integration that moves students beyond the simple regurgitation of ideas and into a higher level of thinking: that of creation.

How To Use This Book

This book is divided into four parts, each designed to help you, the teacher, guide your students in the creation of project-based writing units.

I. Project-Based Writing and the Multi-Genre Approach (pages 9–12)

Here is where you can find an overview of the ideas behind project-based writing and why the multi-genre approach is so vital to engaging your students and enriching their writing.

II. Creating a Project-Based Writing Unit (pages 13–19)

This section shows you how to begin the process of introducing your students to multi-genre projects. This is where you and your students can start to hone in on the topics and themes that most interest them. It's also where you will learn about the elements that make up each project-based writing unit and where you'll get a glimpse at what a finished product could look like.

III. Resources (pages 20–62)

The resources contained within this section are divided into four main categories:

Activities   **Research**   **Organization**   **Assessment**

Collectively — or in any combination you choose — these resources are intended to provide your students with the tools needed to produce projects that are effective, engaging, and unique. Each page is written to the students, and each is designed to serve as a resource your students can refer back to as they work through the creative process. Each new resource in this section begins with a brief statement explaining how it can be helpful in the creation of a project-based writing unit.

A. Activities

Here you'll find the nuts and bolts of any project-based writing unit. These activities are varied and flexible; they span several genres and skills, and they can be introduced in any order. The aim here is to equip your students with an abundance of options and ideas.

B. Research

This section gives your students practical methods for conducting and recording the research they will need to do in order to dig deeper into their topics.

How To Use This Book *(cont.)*

III. Resources *(cont.)*

C. Organization

Students need to pre-plan and structure their work so that they stay focused and on task. The checklists and multiple outlines provided here will help do just that.

D. Assessment

Need a rubric? There are options for different rubrics in this section, as well as a guide to help your students design their own rubrics. Also included is a form that students can use to record your feedback in their own words.

IV. Pre-Made Project-Based Writing Units (pages 63–96)

Finally, this book includes three pre-made project-based writing units that you can use as is, from beginning to end.

For grade 5, the three pre-made units are as follows:

Teach the Teacher

Advocacy Research Project

Historical Advocacy Project

Each unit begins with an overview page that provides step-by-step instructions on how to proceed through the unit. You can also dip into the "Activities" section to add or swap out any lesson you wish. It is this ability to interchange lessons and create different combinations of units that makes this concept of project-based writing with a multi-genre emphasis so unique.

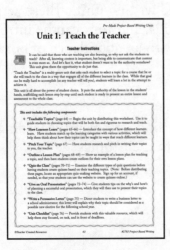

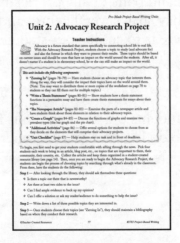

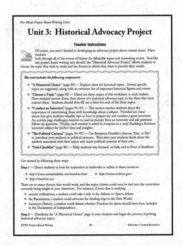

What Is Project-Based Writing?

Project-based writing puts a spin on the concept of project-based learning, which is the act of learning through identifying a real-world problem and developing its solution. The project that results from this endeavor encourages students to use critical-thinking skills to journey towards an authentic goal.

Project-based writing activities strive to meet certain criteria. By design, these activities are . . .

- ❖ multi-genre.
- ❖ differentiated.
- ❖ thematic.
- ❖ both linguistic and non-linguistic.

- ❖ cross-curricular.
- ❖ based on real-world scenarios.
- ❖ guided by student choice.
- ❖ filled with 21st-century connections.

Project-based writing argues that any subject — be it language arts or STEM — can benefit from strong writing practice. Any genre of writing can support the other. And any engaging activity that links academic learning to the real world can be a 21st-century tool.

10 Reasons to Teach Project-Based Writing

1. It is an organic way to integrate all core subjects — math, science, history, and language arts.

2. It proves to students that imagination and creativity are connected to research and expository writing.

3. It hits all the major elements of the higher levels of Bloom's Taxonomy: Analysis, Evaluation, and Creation.

4. By allowing students to choose their format of showing what they know, the buy-in for the quality of the final project is tremendous.

5. Students develop projects that are individualized, unique, and specific from each other.

6. It is a powerful way to incorporate all multiple intelligences: visual, verbal, logical, musical, physical, social, solitary, and naturalistic.

7. It desegregates nonfiction and fiction, blending the two.

8. It integrates the core subjects with non-core subjects, potentially using technology, art, music, etc.

9. It is a rigorous assessment requiring high levels of thought and communication.

10. It requires use of the entire writing process — from brainstorming to revising, editing, and completing the final draft — regardless of the genres picked and the topic chosen.

The Multi-Genre Approach

At the heart of project-based writing is the concept of melding multiple genres into a final product. This multi-genre approach involves taking several distinct types of writing and fusing them into something unique and powerful. Essentially, a hybrid is created.

Throughout history, humans have strived to create hybrids. In science, people have bred their ideal loyal companion in the Golden Retriever or created their perfect salad accessory in the bug-resistant tomato. In literature, authors and storytellers have written about hybrids, such as the unicorn and Pegasus.

Here are some examples of hybrids throughout history:

Picture	Description
	half electric, half gasoline-powered
	half person, half fish
	half Labrador, half poodle
	half chocolate, half peanut butter

In project-based writing, a hybrid is created when we combine genres that revolve around a shared topic or theme. The result is a multi-genre project that uses the best of different presentations and weaves them together into a totally new creature.

After all, just as any subject can benefit from strong writing practice, so can any genre of writing help support another. The multi-genre aspect of project-based writing is important because it is vital that students understand that genres are not compartmentalized in life. For example, a narrative can support a persuasive argument, just as a graph can support a summary. Weaving the strengths of multiple genres together into one project is the key to project-based writing and to providing one's audience with a richer, fuller picture of a topic or theme.

Differentiation in Education

As you know, there are many different kinds of learners out there in the classrooms. Some students like to write, others like to sing; some like to play sports, while others like to draw. A multi-genre approach allows students to choose ways to show off what they know and what they've learned about a topic, using the methods that are the most interesting to them. Just as importantly, it allows them to challenge themselves and present topics using methods that are not normally in their nature to attempt. So by requiring students to display their content knowledge in multiple ways, you are allowing them to operate within their comfort zones on the one hand, while also pushing them to more fully develop a technique that is challenging to them.

21st Century Connection: Many students know what interests them, what kind of learner they are, and how they most like to display their knowledge. But it's also very empowering for them to take quizzes that help them identify their natural instincts. With that in mind, consider having students take a test to identify the style in which they learn best. One such four-part quiz is available at The George Lucas Foundation's website, Edutopia.org:

http://www.edutopia.org/multiple-intelligences-learning-styles-quiz

PAGE 1 OF 4

How much time do you spend:

	NONE	ONLY A LITTLE	A FAIR AMOUNT	A LOT	ALL THE TIME
Getting lost in a good book.	○	○	○	○	○
Doing crafts or arts projects.	○	○	○	○	○
Trying to solve mysteries, riddles, or crossword puzzles.	○	○	○	○	○
Writing a journal or blogging.	○	○	○	○	○
Reflecting on your life and your future.	○	○	○	○	○
Playing sports.	○	○	○	○	○
Yearning to spend time with nature.	○	○	○	○	○

(Next Page >)

See page 12 for a complete breakdown of the different types of learners that you may have in your classroom.

Differentiation in Education *(cont.)*

Because we hear so much about differentiation in education, let's take a moment to look more closely at the different ways people learn—and just as importantly for purposes of project-based writing, the different ways people best show what they've learned. This information is usually referred to as "multiple intelligences." Consult the following chart:

The Multiple Intelligences	Some Ways They Learn/Show What They Know
Visual/Spatial	puzzles, maps, 3-D models, charts, graphs, architecture
Verbal/Linguistic	reading, word games, poetry, speeches, lectures
Logical/Mathematical	patterns, puzzles, experiments, investigations, mysteries
Musical/Auditory	songs, lyrics, rhythmic speaking, dance, musical instruments
Physical/Kinesthetic	movement, hands-on activities, acting out, role-playing, realia
Social/Interpersonal	interaction, dialogue, group dynamics, e-mail, video conferencing
Solitary/Intrapersonal	introspection, diaries, journals, books, independent study
Naturalistic	walks; digging; collecting; using microscopes, telescopes, maps, and globes

Choosing a Topic or Theme

The first step a student must take in creating a project-based writing unit is choosing a topic that piques his or her interest. When thinking about a topic, the student might want to choose one with which he or she is somewhat familiar but could learn more about through research. On the other hand, the student could choose a topic he or she has always wanted to know more about but hasn't had the opportunity to explore in detail.

An ideal topic could be anything from a historical event or person to a hot-topic issue that the student wishes to advocate for or argue against.

A theme-based project is another option to consider. Themes, however, can often be discovered and uncovered midway through a topic-based project. (For an activity page on revealing themes, see pages 24–25 in the "Resources" section.)

Where to Find Topics

Topics are always out there, ready to be dissected and discussed. Here are just a few of the many possibilities you can present to your students:

❖ **Historical Events or People** — Salem Witch Trials • Declaration of Independence • Underground Railroad • Emancipation Proclamation • The Boston Tea Party • The American Revolution • Abraham Lincoln • King Charles I • Founding Fathers • Benjamin Franklin • Halley's Comet

❖ **Writers/Artists/Scientists** — Thomas Jefferson • Anne Bradstreet • Benjamin Banneker • Christopher Paul Curtis • J.K. Rowling

❖ **Recent Events or People** — September 11, 2001 • The Dot-Com Bubble • The Housing Boom and Crash • Bill Gates • Barack Obama • Lance Armstrong • Muhammad Ali • Danica Patrick • Hurricane Katrina • Japan Earthquake and Tsunami of 2011

> *See page 14 for a great way to create a collaborative classroom resource library!*

❖ **Advocacy Issues** — Single-Sex Schools • Paying Students for Grades • Paying Students for Attendance • Global Warming • School Budgets • Cloning • Dress Code • Gum-Chewing • Cell-Phone Usage

❖ **Themes** — Change • Courage • Acceptance • Loyalty • Success • Aging • Overcoming Adversity

❖ **Morals** — "Beauty is only skin deep." • "Birds of a feather flock together." • "Live and let live." • "Look before you leap."

You may choose to present these to your class, or you could opt for topics that align more closely with your class's curriculum. A list of possible topics could serve as a way to jumpstart your students' thought processes about what kinds of subjects would provide the basis for dynamic project-based writing units.

The Student-Created Resource Library

It's true that you can use the traditional way of having students find their sources, research their topics, and collect their data. But instead, consider making research a collaborative, community-building project for the entire classroom.

Imagine an area of the classroom filled with the resources brought in by the students. As students discover reference material, articles, and chapters from outside the classroom, they bring copies of the material into the classroom and file them in this location for other students to use.

It's easy to start. First, assign a typical advocacy topic that can be found in many different formats. Take, for example, the topic of global warming. Okay, so you've asked students to bring in copies of articles, book pages, etc., all on global warming. Create a file called "Global Warming" and place it in a special file box called "Resource Library." File all of the resources into it.

Try it as a weekly current-events assignment leading up to a research report. It's possible that by the time the students have to actually select a topic, you will have a resource library already underway for that topic.

The great part of this is that it's a growing, dynamic library. As kids settle on their topics, they continue to research and add to the files.

In addition, to encourage further collaboration, keep a chart in the classroom with everyone's names and selected topics so that when students come across research that relates to a peer's topic, they can refer that student to the evidence they found. It's a collaborative form of research that uses the classroom as a working, growing reference library.

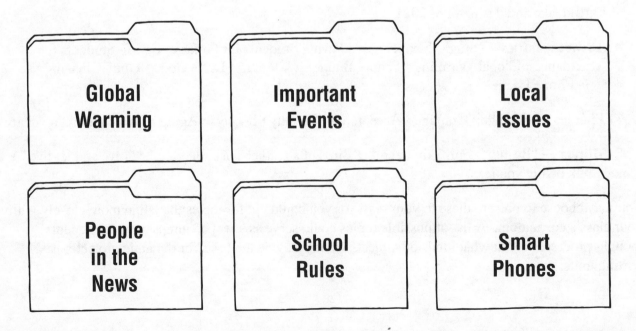

What Are the Parts of a Unit?

In order to create a project-based writing unit, students will use many skills and work in multiple genres. They will do this in all of the steps of the creation process, from planning and research to writing and the production of a final project. This final product will consist of two basic parts: the multi-genre elements and the container.

> *See pages 18–19 for examples of containers and the multi-genre elements they could contain.*

The Multi-Genre Elements

Once students choose the topic or theme on which they will build their projects, they next should begin to think about what elements will make up their final project. These multi-genre elements will comprise the bulk of the project, and they will ideally be a mixture of multiple written and visual genres. In order to really challenge themselves (and also explore more nuances of their topics and themes), students should work not just with the elements with which they are most comfortable. While a visual learner is encouraged to use all of the elements that align with his or her instinctual abilities (say, creating comic books and designing website homepages), that student is also expected to consider penning a persuasive essay or crafting a campaign speech that further illuminates the topic.

A list of possible multi-genre elements is included on the following page. While there is some overlap, the elements are divided into columns depending on whether they are primarily written or visual. You may wish to copy this list and distribute one to each student. Have your students examine

> *Many of these elements are explored individually and in greater detail on pages 20–47 of the "Activities" section.*

each column and circle those activities that they may find interesting to create and that will best illustrate their chosen issue or topic. Also, allow students to add new ideas to the list. As long as the element enriches their project, students should be encouraged to let their imaginations soar.

The Container

One important guiding principle for students to keep in mind is that a project's final appearance will function best if it reflects the theme or subject that it is based on. An appropriate container will go a long way in accomplishing this. Whether it is simple or elaborate, it should function as the final piece that ties all of the other pieces together. Think of the container as the visual delivery system for the project.

A List of Multi-Genre Elements

Directions: Below are lists of possible elements you can combine for use in a project. Examine each column and circle the ones that you may find interesting to create and that will best illustrate your chosen issue or topic. If any other ideas occur to you, record them in the spaces at the bottom of the appropriate column.

Written (Linguistic)	Visual (Non-Linguistic)	Other
Campaign Speech	Advertisement	Directions
Character Sketch	Family Tree	Recipe
Dialogue	Greeting Card	Quiz
Essay	Website	How-to Guide
Fable or Fairy Tale	Picture Book	List
Website	Map	Song
Poetry	Postcard	Dance
Diary Entry	Movie Poster	Board Game
Blog	Diorama	Computer Game
Memoir	Flip Book	Reader's Theater
News Article	Building-Blocks Structure	Podcast
Op-ed Piece	Statue	Video
Petition	Comic Book	Monologue
Advocacy Essay	Comic Life (using iLife suite)	
Letters	Prezi	
Review	PowerPoint	
Script	Blueprint (using Google Sketch-up)	
Glossary		
Narrative		
Interview		
Legend		
Letter of Complaint		
Summary		

Using a Unit Checklist

A checklist is an effective organizational tool that can help students remember what's due and when. There are many different ways to format a checklist. The three pre-made units in this workbook (pages 63–96), for example, contain checklists that are tailored to those projects.

The sample checklist below can give you an idea of appropriate expectations you could have for each student to include in his or her writing unit. For the project below, you may instruct students that the top three assignments must be included. From there, they could be asked to choose one activity from each of the other categories, ensuring that the completed project contains seven pieces in all. This is just one way to approach assigning a unit's components.

Note: A blank checklist is provided on page 58 in the "Resources" section.

Date Due	Date Completed	Assigned Element	Possibilities
		Persuasive Pitch to Teacher About Topic	❖ Letter ❖ Essay
		Research	❖ Cornell Notes ❖ Quickwrites ❖ Movement Survey
		Bibliography/Works Cited	❖ n/a
		Written Piece	❖ Narrative ❖ Poem ❖ Glossary/Dictionary ❖ Interview/Dialogue ❖ Biography ❖ Diary Entry
		Visual or Technological Element	❖ Poster/Ad ❖ Cartoon ❖ PowerPoint/Prezi ❖ Website ❖ Board Game
		Mathematical Piece	❖ Map ❖ Recipe ❖ Step-by-Step Guide
		Musical- or Movement-Based Piece	❖ Cover Song ❖ Original Song ❖ Dance

What Will a Completed Project Look Like?

So what should a completed project-based writing unit look like? The short answer is that there is no one design for how these units should look. In fact, the hope is that each student project looks unique in its display and is specific in its content. Individuality is not only encouraged, it is essential to the concept.

Below and on page 19 are some examples:

Project Topic/Theme: Childhood Obesity   **Container/Format:** Pizza Box

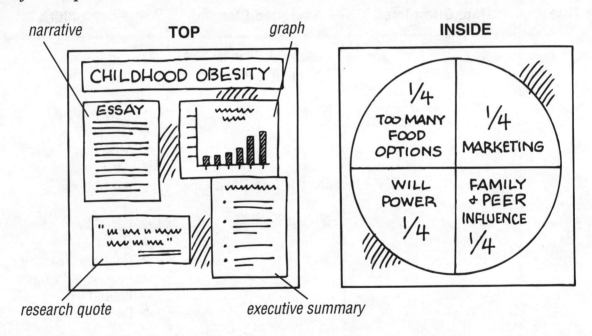

Project Topic/Theme: Pollution   **Container/Format:** Tri-Board Display

Includes: *a research paper on pollution, a science-fiction narrative about a future in which the world has been taken over by trash, comic-book frames illustrating key moments from the narrative, a recipe of the ingredients that make up a dump site, a student-created quiz, the answers to which can be found in the contents of the project*

What Will a Completed Project Look Like? *(cont.)*

Project Topic/Theme: Change Is a Constant   **Container/Format:** Homepage/Website

Includes: *an embedded video showing an animated movie of Pangaea and the concept of plate tectonics, a fictitious diary entry from a character as a young girl and as an older woman, an analysis of a quote by Benjamin Franklin ("When you're finished changing, you're finished."), a list of research-based strategies a student can use to improve his/her IQ.*

Project Topic/Theme: "The Balance of Power in the U.S. Government"
Container/Format: Quilt

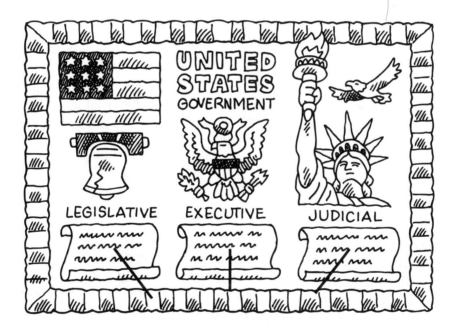

Scrolls featuring different writing genres

Playing Think–Tac–Toe

 Project-Based Writing Connection: Use this resource as a brainstorming activity or to help you begin rough drafts for your projects.

Get your creative juices flowing by using these prompts to write about your topic.

Directions: Pick three prompts in a row — either across or diagonally — and follow the directions. Use a separate piece of paper for your responses.

	Narrative	**Response to Literature**	**Persuasive**
Row 1	Write a story in which the main character completely changes his or her mind about something important by the end of the story.	Find an essay, poem, or piece of art connected to your topic and respond to the author's main message.	Take a stance on your topic and create an ad that displays your stance.
Row 2	Write a story that begins in the middle of an action-packed scene related to your topic.	Find a blog, letter, column, or poem connected to your issue. Rewrite it any way you want. Then write a note explaining what you changed and why.	In a one-page essay, take a stance on your topic and persuade the reader to agree with you.
Row 3	Make up a fairy tale about your topic. Include a moral or lesson at the end.	Find a story, poem, or piece of art connected to your topic and write an analysis of the main character's traits.	Write a persuasive letter to your school principal about your topic.

Getting a Reader's Attention

Project-Based Writing Connection: When adding a written component to your project, use a hook to grab your reader's attention right from the start.

A *hook* is that first moment of a paper — be it a narrative or an essay — that catches the reader's attention and makes him or her want to read more.

Below is a list of hooks using different strategies to begin the same essay: a piece written about the lost colony of Roanoke. As you can see, there are many ways to hook a reader.

Definition A colony is defined as a group of people who leave their native land to settle in a land with the intent on remaining connected to its original country.	**Onomatopoeia** Scratch. Scritch. The settler quickly etched the mysterious message into the tree never to know if it was going to be seen by another human.
Dialogue "Where are they all?" the first mate whispered, chills covering the sailors as they each thought about the disappearance of the people who should have been there to greet them.	**Simile/Metaphor** When Capt. John White landed back in Roanoke in 1590, he was greeted with a mystery as deep as the sea on which he had sailed.
Fact/Statistic In the late 16th Century, 110 men, women, and children made the brave journey to the New World.	**Staccato Three-Word Lead** Men. Woman. Children. They all disappeared without a trace, leaving us to solve the mystery of their whereabouts.
In the Middle of the Action As the ship dropped anchor and the vessel slowly glided to a halt, the men, women, and children all gathered on the deck for a first look at their new home.	**Theme** Traveling to the New World was dangerous, but the people of Roanoke left us a mystery of those dangers that would haunt historians for years to come.

Directions: After reading each of the examples above, think of an essay you are working on. You may be revising or just beginning. Try to start the piece of writing using each of these strategies. Then, pass your new list of hooks to your classmate or to an adult family member. Have him or her circle the three he or she feels are the strongest. Pick one of these three hooks to use when writing or revising.

Comparing Skills: Paraphrasing vs. Summarizing

 Project-Based Writing Connection: Paraphrasing and summarizing are important skills to master; each will help you create unique writing pieces for any project.

Summarizing and *paraphrasing* are two different skills, each with its own purpose.

Think of them this way:

Summarizing	**Paraphrasing**
finding the most important points and *only including those main ideas*	giving a beat-for-beat translation of a piece of writing *using only your own words*

In order to remember which one is which, think of the first letter of each word:

❖ **S**ummarizing is **s**horter. You only use the main idea from the piece.

❖ **P**araphrasing **p**uts it into your own words, sentence by sentence.

Directions: In the following activity, you are going to show the differences between summarizing and paraphrasing by using the same paragraph to show an example of both.

On a separate piece of paper, create a dual-entry journal. Title one side "Summarized" and the other "Paraphrased." Use the following paragraph as your informational text:

> *In 1587, the Roanoke Colony was founded on Roanoke Island in what is now present-day North Carolina. It was created to establish a permanent English settlement in the Virginia Colony. Funded by Sir Walter Raleigh, the Roanoke Colony was begun with the help of 110 men, women, and children. It was at the Roanoke Colony that the first English-speaking child, Virginia Dare, was born in the New World. Soon after the settler's arrival, however, Capt. John White was forced to return to England to get food supplies. Travel was difficult, and it took him nearly three years to return to Roanoke. By the time he returned, the entire colony was deserted. To this day, what became of the settlers remains a mystery.*

Squeezing a Summary

Project-Based Writing Connection: Summarizing can help you persuade a reader, analyze an argument, or move a story along. It's a crossover skill that aids many genres.

Creating a summary is an important skill because it allows you to boil a piece of writing down to its essential message.

Directions: In the following activity, you are going to challenge yourself to squeeze a piece of writing down to its bare essentials. The rules are as follows:

1. The initial paragraph must be stripped down to fit in the space provided below.

2. First cross out information that you feel is too specific to be an important detail.

3. You must use your own words.

4. You must use complete sentences.

Here is the initial paragraph:

> *In 1700, Bartolomeo Cristofori of Florence, Italy invented a new musical instrument, unseen by anyone before. The sound created by this massive creation was made by tapping leather-covered hammers. These hammers in turn struck strings within the body of the instrument. This permitted the player to control the volume of the notes, creating tone, mood, and expression in a unique way. The instrument was called the piano.*

Take just the gist of the paragraph and squeeze the key information into this box:

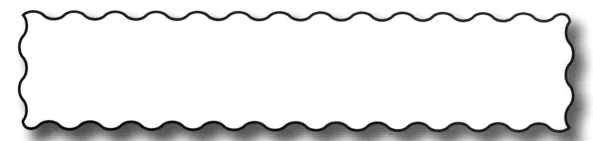

Added Challenge: Now really whittle down what you just wrote. Cross out most of the details until only the most essential information remains. What you have left should fit inside this new box.

Revealing a Theme

> **Project-Based Writing Connection:** Take your final project up a notch by adding an overall theme that represents your work and by displaying it in an interesting way.

A theme can be a concept like "Good vs. Evil," or a theme might be a moral like "Never judge a book by its cover." By weaving a strong theme throughout your project, you can really add an extra dimension to it. Think of the theme as the icing on your project's cake, the gravy on its meatloaf.

Perhaps you've planned from the beginning to incorporate a specific theme into your project. If so, you've made sure to sprinkle it throughout all of your pieces. However, there might be another way to go about things. You might be able to look closely at your various pieces and . . . surprise, the theme was there all along! Finding the theme can be a bit like a scavenger hunt.

Once you do settle on your theme, find a way to insert it all over the place. It should be a repeating message throughout your project, a treasure hunt for your audience to find in each piece of your writing.

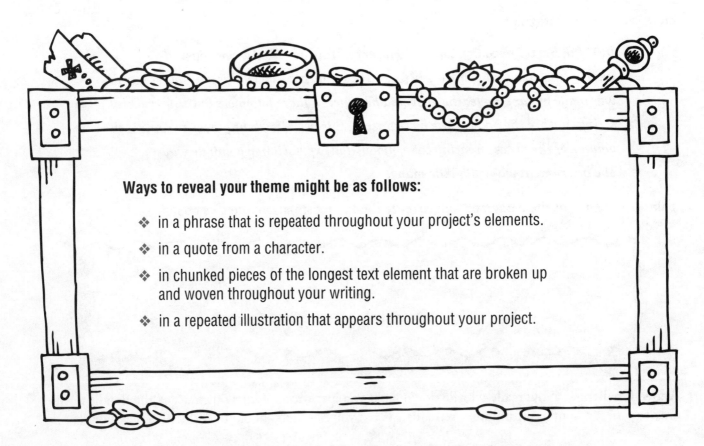

Ways to reveal your theme might be as follows:

❖ in a phrase that is repeated throughout your project's elements.

❖ in a quote from a character.

❖ in chunked pieces of the longest text element that are broken up and woven throughout your writing.

❖ in a repeated illustration that appears throughout your project.

Repeating a theme in your pieces helps your reader see the thought that went into your writing. In order to see how revealing a theme might work, complete the activity on the following page.

Revealing a Theme *(cont.)*

Directions: First, look at this list of possible themes:

> **1.** The Will to Survive

> **3.** The Circle of Life

> **2.** The Power of Words

> **4.** Anyone Can Make a Difference

Now, look at the three excerpts from a student's multi-genre project below:

Story

Ben's Surprising Summer

Ben started his summer not giving a second thought to the owls in the woods, but by September he had rescued the nest and saved the trees from being cut down.

Essay

Dwindling Resources

The grasslands soon evolved from a rich area of wildlife to an area with no plants, no animals, and no resources. The question then became, "How could the lands be transformed back into what they once were?"

Comic Strip

VACANCY: SPACE AVAILABLE

From the four themes above, which one do you think best describes the samples when examined together? Write your response on the line below.

_____

_____

"Finding" a Poem

 Project-Based Writing Connection: By focusing on a key line or phrase that recurs throughout your project, you can create a found poem that will tie the elements together.

A found poem combines your original poetry with a repeating line that is not very poem-like. To create a found poem, you first have to "find" a phrase that you believe really rings true to the heart of your project's topic or theme. You can find lines like that in many unusual places. Here are just a few spots to look:

- directions
- recipes
- horoscopes
- fortune cookies

- references
- ads
- letters
- e-mails

- catalogues
- textbooks
- cartoons
- cereal boxes

For example, let's say you are studying American history and are writing a poem that describes some aspect of the American Revolution. In your search for inspiration, you go into your pantry at home and look at a box of breakfast cereal. The phrase "A Great Way to Wake Up in the Morning" catches your eye. What would a poem based on that phrase look like? How could you tie in that phrase with your historical topic? That's the challenge of creating a found poem.

Directions: Follow each step below to create a found poem.

Step 1: Begin by choosing one of these topics:

- parents
- chores

- video games
- allergies

- cell phones
- homework

Step 2: You will next need to find a phrase to repeat throughout your poem. Look anywhere in the classroom for your inspiration. Look at the posters on the walls, flip through your textbook, or search through the classroom library. All it takes is one phrase to catch your eye and capture your imagination. Write your phrase here:

Step 3: On a separate piece of paper, write a poem with at least four stanzas. Stay focused on your topic, but also remember to pepper your phrase throughout your poem. By combining these two elements — your topic and your phrase — you can create an interesting and unique final product.

Creating Literary Hybrids

 Project-Based Writing Connection: By understanding the different literary genres, you can select one that will be most effective in helping you get your project's message across.

Just like Dr. Frankenstein's creation was the sum of different parts, a literary hybrid takes two or more literary genres and stitches them together to create a great story. But before you can combine genres to create a hybrid, you need to think about the distinct elements that make up each genre.

Directions: Identify the main elements of the genres listed below. Think about everything from setting and format to tone and plot. Include an example of each genre. The first one has been done for you.

1. Mythology	2. Young Adult
❖ gods/goddesses ❖ explanation of natural occurrences ❖ created by ancient cultures ❖ emotions can be represented by people ❖ heroes **Example:** elements in *The Lightning Thief*	 **Example:**
3. Mystery	4. Memoir
    Example:	 **Example:**
5. Science Fiction	6. Biography
     Example:	 **Example:**

Now that you've analyzed these genres, think about how you respond to them. Which ones do you most like to read or write? Choose two, and circle them. On a separate page, write a narrative that smooshes together the elements of your two chosen genres. Have fun creating a whole new literary species!

Teacher Note: Another way to do this would be to roll a single die twice. The genres are numbered above. Use the results of your rolls to identify the two genres students must use to create a hybrid.

Conducting a Movement Survey

 Project-Based Writing Connection: This activity will help you do research by gauging public opinion about a topic.

In this activity, your class will vote on issues with their bodies by moving to different areas in the classroom. This offers you a quick, visual way of "taking the temperature of the class" on important issues. After conducting the survey, hold a class discussion about the results. This will allow your classmates to explain their choices.

Tip: Conduct the survey twice: once *before* your classmates learn more about the topic (in order to gauge prior knowledge), and once *after* you have presented evidence about the topic (in order to see if their opinions have changed).

For example, imagine that the topic is "dress codes in school." Let's say you are already researching the pros and cons of a school dress code, but you would like to know the opinion of the class before you present any evidence to them.

Here is some language that you can use to conduct a movement survey:

Before you all came into the classroom, I put up two signs: one says "Pro," and the other says "Con." You can see them on either side of the room.

The topic I'm going to be discussing is whether or not schools should have a dress code.

When I give you the signal, you can vote by standing under the sign that matches your opinion.

- ❖ If you believe that there is a reason that schools should have a dress code, please quietly go stand under the "Pro" sign.

- ❖ If you believe, without a doubt, that schools should not have a dress code, then go stand under the "Con" sign.

- ❖ If you are undecided, please go stand in the middle of the two groups in the back of the room.

Directions: Use the form on page 30 to conduct a movement survey in your classroom. Reference the cheat sheet provided on page 29 in order to lead a respectful, informative classroom discussion about the results of the survey.

Conducting a Movement Survey *(cont.)*

After conducting the movement survey, you can then lead the class in a discussion about the results. When you permit the participants in the survey to give their rationale for choosing the sides they did, this will provide you with further evidence for your research project. Take notes on what people say, and write down direct quotes whenever possible.

When conducting the discussion part of your survey, it's important to allow one side to talk and the other side to respond *to that point alone*. This is called "refutation," and it is a vital part of a persuasive counterargument. A back-and-forth exchange of dialogue on a key point might look like this:

Student A: The dress code is important because it puts us all on an even level of appearance.

Student B: That's an interesting point, and I agree that it evens things out, but it doesn't allow for individuality and diversity in appearance.

Use this cheat sheet to keep the discussion respectful and on track:

Here are some guidelines your classmates should keep in mind:

❖ You are agreeing and disagreeing with points, not with people.

❖ If you disagree with a point, that doesn't mean the point isn't important.

❖ People are more likely to listen if you are diplomatic and respectful.

Here are some sentence stems for discussion:

To disagree:

❖ I realize not everyone will agree with me, but . . .

❖ That's an interesting idea, but maybe . . .

❖ I see it a little differently because . . .

To agree:

❖ I agree with what _____ said about . . .

❖ I was wondering/thinking about that, too.

❖ Can I just take that point a step further and say that . . .

To encourage participation:

❖ We haven't heard from you yet.

❖ Could you give me an example of that?

To add to the thought:

❖ May I add something here?

❖ Maybe you could . . .

To clarify:

❖ Could you repeat/rephrase that?

❖ In other words, you think that . . .

Conducting a Movement Survey *(cont.)*

A movement survey is a way for you to conduct a poll by asking people to stand in a place that represents their opinion on a topic.

Step 1:

On the day *before* the activity, write down a little information to read to your pollsters to give them the context of your topic:

❖ Write one sentence that argues **FOR** a side: _____

_____

❖ Write one sentence that argues **AGAINST** that side: _____

_____

❖ Write a question you want to ask your pollsters: _____

_____

Step 2:

On the day of the activity, hang a sign in the room on one wall marked "PRO." Put a sign marked "CON" on the opposite wall. You can decorate your sign with symbols about your topic.

Step 3:

Read your information to your pollsters to give them background information on your topic.

Step 4:

Ask students to go stand under the sign that best represents their opinion.

Step 5:

Ask people to give other reasons why they believe the way they do. If you write down the best argument you hear word-for-word, you can use the quote as evidence in your essay.

Number of students who stood under the **PRO** sign: _____

❖ The best argument from the **PRO** side: _____

_____

Number of students who stood under the **CON** sign: _____

❖ The best argument from the **CON** side: _____

_____

Use the information above as evidence for your research, advocacy, or persuasive essays.

Using Technology to Present

 Project-Based Writing Connection: Use a 21st-century, technology-based method to present your project in a way that adds extra appeal for your audience.

These days, we don't just explain what we know through oral presentations or the traditional book report; we use technology to display and communicate our knowledge.

Think about what you would want to watch or listen to or read, and then go ahead and create that for your work. Listed below are three possible ways you can display what you've learned in a method that reflects the age you live in, the Age of Technology:

❖ **Set Up a Screencast** — Using an iPad app like Educreator or ShowMe, you can display an image and record narration. You can then submit it from your tablet directly to the website. A link will be provided, which you can submit to your teacher for viewing.

Example: Let's say your project involves designing your own country. Open up a screencasting app and draw the map of your country. Include borders, the most important cities, symbols to represent resources, and icons to represent geographical features. Narrate as you draw so that your viewers can hear your description of the country. Mention facts and statistics like population and political system. When you are done, send it to the main site and share the link with your class.

❖ **Produce a Prezi** — A Prezi is a step up from a normal PowerPoint presentation. It uses a concept map rather than slides to go from idea to idea. What's unique about a Prezi is that you can load an image that represents your whole topic and then "zoom in" on the details that show off your knowledge on that topic. If you go to *http://prezi.com*, you can see examples of this cool presentation software. You can create your presentation for free, and it's stored on the web, always there for your teacher to access it.

Example: If your project is about saving an endangered species, you can upload an image of the animal and zoom in on specific features. Zoom in on its eye to learn more about how we see the animal in myths and stories. Zoom in to its claw to learn more about how humans endanger its existence. This will give your audience a micro and macro understanding of your topic.

❖ **Make a Movie** — There are many ways to create a digital movie. Whether you are using iMovie on a Mac or producing a free, web-based, 30-second movie using Animoto, you have options.

Example: Imagine you have written a letter to a local politician about nutrition in school lunches. Let's say you get the chance to meet him and shake his hand. Record your progress through photographs. Get a picture of yourself sending off the letter, shaking his hand, and cutting a ribbon on a new school cafeteria. Whatever your journey through your project was, find visuals to represent each step. Upload them into Animoto, add some copyright-free music from a site like *www.Soundzabound.com*, and watch a 30-second narrative of your work in pictures and music. Send the link to your teacher.

Directions: Let's say your subject is texting while on the move (walking, riding a bicycle, riding a skateboard, etc.). Think about your position on this activity. Then think about which of the above methods would be the best way to give a presentation on this subject. Give a complete answer on a separate piece of paper.

Reading a Website

Project-Based Writing Connection: By looking closely at the elements that make up websites, you can get ideas for ways to incorporate different genres into your projects.

A website is a great example of a multi-genre project. Look at it! It has text, pictures, videos, charts, links . . . you name it. As a student, you need to understand how to read a website. Sometimes it may be difficult to sift through the clutter of words and pictures to locate the information you need. Sometimes you may click on a link in order to further your research, only to be taken to an ad instead. Reading a website may seem easy and natural, but it can actually be tricky.

Directions: Look at the website below.* Use it to answer the questions that follow on the next page.

*Note: This is not a real website.

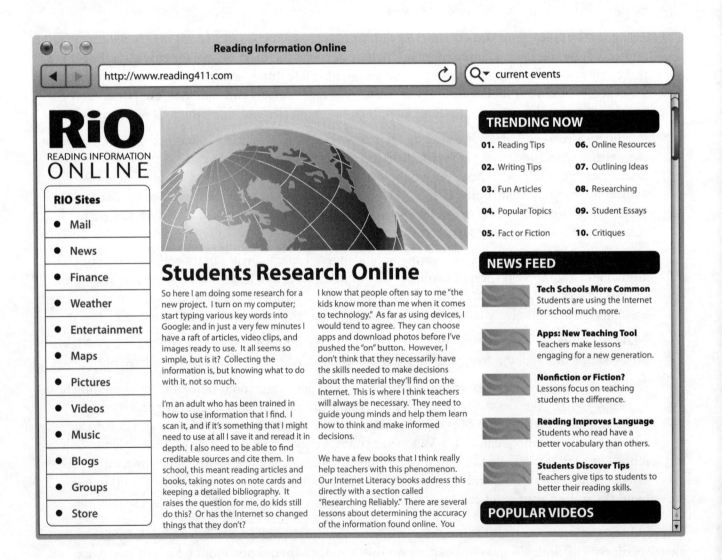

Reading a Website *(cont.)*

Directions: After carefully examining the website on page 32, answer the following questions.

1. What is the name of the website? This is generally located in big letters that draw your eye to them.

   _____

2. What is the website's address (or URL)? You can find this information in the browser window near the top. It usually begins with "http" and/or "www."

   _____

3. What is the name of the featured, or front-page, article?

   _____

4. There are several general categories you can visit by clicking on links from this home page. Name six of them.

   _____   _____   _____

   _____   _____   _____

5. What is the name of the third article displayed in the News Feed?

   _____

6. What is the name of the section that shows the 10 most popular articles on the website currently?

   _____

7. Look at your answer to #6. What is the name of the seventh topic listed in this section?

   _____

- -

Teacher Note: Fold this section under before photocopying this page.

Answers: **1.** Reading Information Online; **2.** http://www.reading411.com; **3.** "Students Research Online"; **4.** Mail, News, Finance, Weather, etc.; **5.** "Nonfiction or Fiction?"; **6.** Trending Now; **7.** Outlining Ideas

Creating a Homepage

 Project-Based Writing Connection: You can use the format of a website's homepage to showcase many different projects related to the same topic or theme.

When it comes to websites—the ultimate multi-genre projects—there's no place like the homepage. A good homepage includes a variety of information and formats, and it invites and entices users to visit all of the other content on the site.

A homepage should have many elements, and they should be laid out in a way that is informative and clear to read.

- ❖ **Banner** — The banner runs along the top of the homepage. It often includes a title, a slogan, and a visual that represents the company/person who runs the website.

- ❖ **Menu Bar** — Often located in the banner, the menu bar lists the main categories that make up the website. These are links that the user can click on to visit those pages/sections of the site (for example, "Home," "Blog," "About," "Resources").

- ❖ **Links to Content** — A good homepage features a lot of interesting pictures and story starters. By clicking on links or pictures, users will then be sent to other pages on the site to read or see more of what interests them.

Directions: In the space below, sketch a rough draft of a homepage for a website about your chosen topic. Include a banner and a menu bar. Below the banner, include text, pictures, and links that would entice visitors to want to read and see more of what is on the other pages of your website.

21st-Century Connection: With parents' or teacher's permission, a student can go online and easily create a website using something like *www.wordpress.com* or *www.edublogs.org*.

Reading and Writing a Script

 Project-Based Writing Connection: You can use the script format to create characters who are affected by, talking about, or in some other way dealing with a topic or theme.

A *script* is a written version of a visually performed medium (a play, a television show, a movie, etc.). In addition to the dialogue (the lines the actors speak), a script also includes the setting (where the action takes place) and stage directions (how the dialogue is spoken, how the actors move through the scene, etc.).

Here's an excerpt from a script for a fantasy movie called *The Treasure of Fairy Cove*.

(PATRICIA stands by the moss-covered tree, looking around for where the sound is coming from. Suddenly, the sound of a flurry of wings explodes from the leaves above her. RIPLEY appears.)

PATRICIA

Ahhhhh!

RIPLEY

(fluttering just within reach)

What are you, wingless creature? Be you goblin or ogre?

PATRICIA

No, I, er…well….

RIPLEY

What is a "noIerwell?" What brings you to Treeline?

(PATRICIA is speechless, which bores RIPLEY. The fairy flies off to join a group of other fairies in the distance. PATRICIA faints, only to wake the next morning in her bed in her room. The creatures are gone. PATRICIA thinks, "Have I been dreaming?")

So to write a script takes the following elements:

1. the character names (in all caps)

2. stage directions (in parentheses)

3. the dialogue (not in quotation marks)

Directions: On a separate sheet of paper, continue the scene by having the two characters exchange some new lines of dialogue. Remember to include the three components — character names, stage directions, and dialogue — formatted properly.

Writing a Recipe for "Success"

Project-Based Writing Connection: Use the format and elements of recipes to examine a theme or topic in a unique way.

We all know what the average recipe looks like, but have you ever thought of using that format to describe the ingredients of something that you couldn't touch or that wasn't meant to be eaten?

Recipes usually include a few standard elements and often look like this:

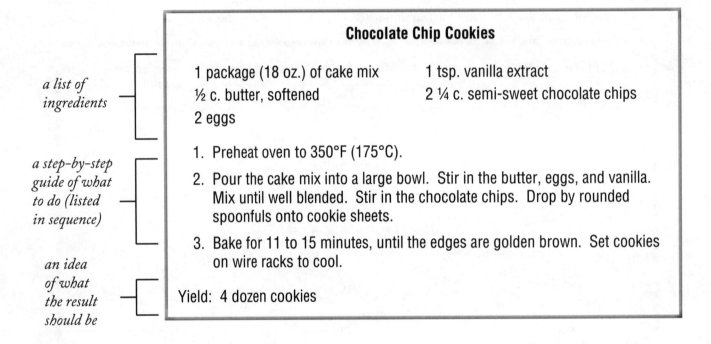

a list of ingredients

a step-by-step guide of what to do (listed in sequence)

an idea of what the result should be

Chocolate Chip Cookies

1 package (18 oz.) of cake mix   1 tsp. vanilla extract
½ c. butter, softened   2 ¼ c. semi-sweet chocolate chips
2 eggs

1. Preheat oven to 350°F (175°C).

2. Pour the cake mix into a large bowl. Stir in the butter, eggs, and vanilla. Mix until well blended. Stir in the chocolate chips. Drop by rounded spoonfuls onto cookie sheets.

3. Bake for 11 to 15 minutes, until the edges are golden brown. Set cookies on wire racks to cool.

Yield: 4 dozen cookies

What if, instead, you were to use the traditional recipe format to describe what goes into something more abstract, like "imagination" or "success"? You would first need to ask yourself the following questions:

❖ What are the ingredients that make up this abstract idea?

❖ How much of each ingredient is required?

❖ How many will the recipe serve?

❖ What are the stove settings and the cooking times?

Directions: Use page 37 to create a recipe for something that can't be eaten or touched.

Writing a Recipe for "Success" *(cont.)*

Directions: It's time to create your own recipe for an intangible thing — that is, something you can't see, touch, taste, or smell.

First, choose one of these invisible, untouchable, untasteable topics. Circle your choice.

Creativity   Hope   Kindness   Intelligence   Friendship   Loyalty   Success

Next, use the template below to create a recipe for your topic. Think about how your chosen topic makes you feel. Don't be afraid to think outside of the box and be creative.

For authenticity, incorporate at least seven of these cooking terms into your recipe:

c. (cup)	stir	pour	sauté
tsp. (teaspoon)	combine	crack	steam
Tbsp. (tablespoon)	whisk	glaze	boil
lb. (pound)	beat	preheat	scald
a pinch	sift	bake	heat
a dash	add	sear	cool

How to Make _____

Ingredients:

To cook:

Yield:

Writing a Resume

Project-Based Writing Connection: Use this resource to create a resume for a fictitious character or historical figure related to your topic.

When someone applies for a job, that person usually brings a resume to the job interview. A *resume* is a one-page snapshot of the applicant's contact information, experience, and education.

Here is an example of a resume:

Joe Job Hunter
12345 Career Quest Ln.
510-555-3445
jjhuntersrus@email.com

Objective: to find a position that utilizes my scientific research abilities, as well as my experience in marine biology

Experience:

October 2010–present

Oceanography Institute of Technology
- Recorded and illustrated species of large sea mammals
- Narwhal expert

April 2009–October 2010

Sea World
- Served as veterinary assistant to all small sea mammals
- Cleaned jellyfish tanks weekly
- Fed otters

Education:

College: BA University of the Pacific '07

High School: Atlantic High School '03

Awards:

Voted Most Likely to Kiss a Shark • Recipient of the Merman of the Year Award

Skills:

Swimming, Diving, Scuba Diving, Drawing, Computer (Word, Excel, PowerPoint), Driving a Submarine

---

Directions: Use the above format to create a resume of your own on page 39.

Writing a Resume *(cont.)*

Directions: Create a resume for an original character or a historical figure. The resume should help describe that character to a reader. When you write a resume, make sure that the reader can easily understand the categories of information. (Use the sample resume on page 38 for assistance.) You may also want to vary the fonts and use **bolds** and *italics*.

name →

address →

phone # →

e-mail address →

_____

_____

_____

_____

Objective: _____

_____

Experience:

Write dates in left-hand column; write job titles and descriptions in the right-hand column.

_____

_____

_____

_____

_____

Education:

_____

_____

Awards:

_____

Skills:

_____

Mimicking an Artist's Style

Project-Based Writing Connection: Use this skill to illustrate a topic or a theme in your project, or to provide insight into cultural aspects of a time period.

You can find art by famous artists that mirrors the subject matter, theme, time period, or mood of a project. You can also create art in the style of the artist you choose. This activity will help you learn about some of the amazing artists out there and will teach you a method for studying an artist's style.

You are going to be asked to a mimic one particular artist. Working with a partner, you will need to identify the qualities that are seen in many of that artist's work and copy those into an original piece you will create.

Directions:

1. Find a partner and draw an artist's name out of a hat. On the sheet, you will see a list of three pieces by that artist. Write the name of the artist and the titles of the art here:

   _____

   _____

2. Find out a little bit about this artist and take notes on the back of this paper. When did he or she live? What was his or her painting style called? Did he or she work with things other than paint and canvas? Can you learn anything about why this artist painted the way he or she did?

3. Look at the paintings by this artist online (and if you are able, print them out). In your notes on the back of this page, create a list of at least five characteristics that can be found in some or all of the pieces. Consider elements such as color palette, use of space, subject matter, medium, mood, and style.

4. Copy the most important information from steps 1, 2, and 3 neatly onto a notecard or other piece of paper.

5. On a blank piece of paper, work with your partner to create a piece of art that is like the artist's work, using the five characteristics as a guide. You can even include things from one or more of the paintings as long as your art is mostly original.

6. The class will set up a gallery where everyone can appreciate and learn about the different qualities in all the studied artists. Name your art and put it up on the wall along with the sheet of information you have prepared.

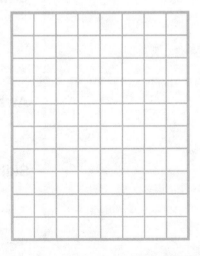

Another Idea: If you do not wish to create original artwork, you can reproduce a piece of art using a grid as a guide. On a copy of one of the paintings, lay out a grid. Then, on an 8 ½" x 11" sheet of paper, use the squares of the grid as a guide to sketch out one of the paintings into a duplicate. Color in your re-creation of the artist's work.

Name: _____

Mimicking an Artist's Style *(cont.)*

Directions: Here is a list of artists to research.

Artist's Name	Names of Some Famous Works
Judith Francisca Baca	*Hands, Farmworkers of Guadalupe, A Vision of the Future Without Fear*
Salvador Dalí	*The Persistence of Memory, Departure of the Winged Ship, Sleep*
Vincent van Gogh	*Self-portrait with Bandaged Ear, Bedroom in Arles, The Starry Night*
Katsushika Hokusai	*The Great Wave of Kanagawa, Red Fuji, Travellers Crossing the Oi River*
Roy Lichtenstein	*Blam, In the Car, Bananas and Grapefruit No. 1*
Henri Matisse	*Woman with a Hat, The Dessert: Harmony in Red, Self-Portrait in a Striped T-shirt*
Grandma Moses	*Sugaring Off, Checkered House, Wash Day*
Georgia O'Keeffe	*Ram's Head White Hollyhock and Little Hills, Sky Above Clouds III, Black Iris*
Abdoulaye Konaté	*Symphonie Bleue (Symphony in Blue), Les Marcheurs (The Walkers), Les Musiciens Koroduga (The Musicians of Koroduga)*
Piet Mondrian	*Red Tree, Gray Tree, Composition A*
Faith Ringgold	*The Civil Rights Triangle, We Came to America, Dancing at the Louvre*
Norman Rockwell	*The Problem We All Live With, Sunset, Rosie the Riveter*
Ibrahim El-Salahi	*Dry Month of the Fast, Ruins of Sawakin, The Last Sound*
Andy Warhol	*A Shot of Marilyn Monroe, Campbell's Soup Cans, Cow Pink on Yellow*
James McNeill Whistler	*Arrangement in Gray and Black No. 1, Nocturne in Black and Gold; Symphony in White, No. 1: The White Girl*
Grant Wood	*American Gothic, New Road, Spring in the Country*
Qiu Ying	*The Imperial Examinations, Spring Morning in the Han Palace, Resting under Willow Trees with a Zither*

Using an Illuminated Letter

Project-Based Writing Connection: You can use an illuminated letter to add a visual element to the final draft of a written piece.

An *illuminated letter* is an illustration of a letter, often the first letter of chapter or book. Symbols and icons are drawn into the letter as a way of visually displaying the idea of the text that follows. An example would be from the Colonial Era, when the illuminated letter was used in many school primers to allow children to understand the main idea of the text even if they couldn't read. For instance, let's say that the book contained the Mother Goose rhyme "Jack Sprat" and was aimed at teaching children not to waste food. The first letter of the book might look like the image to the right:

Illuminated letters use symbols to give visual hints to the reader. You can use this idea in your projects. An illuminated letter is a great way to illustrate your main idea in a piece of writing.

Directions: Look at the illuminated letter to the right. If you saw this letter appear at the start of an essay, what do you think the essay would be about? Write your predictions on the lines that follow.

_____

_____

_____

_____

Now, let's practice this concept by creating an illuminated letter based on a topic you know a lot about: yourself. Using the first letter of your first name, create a block letter. Then design and fill the rest of the space with symbols that represent you.

Using an Illuminated Border

Project-Based Writing Connection: To visually tie a project together, add a border around the final draft of your writing or around the container that houses your project.

Much like an illuminated letter, an *illuminated border* can be used to add visual meaning to a written piece. However, by using the margins of a document, an illuminated border frames the text. It creates a decorative picture around the page. This allows the artist to depict not only symbols, but also landscapes or scenes, much in the same way a comic-book artist of today will sequence a story.

Remember, the illuminated border always stays focused on the main idea of the text.

Directions: Look at the page below. Inside the page, there is a paragraph about the Stamp Act. In the framed border surrounding the paragraph, create an illuminated border that captures the main idea of the paragraph.

> *In 1765, the British Parliament passed the Stamp Act. This piece of legislature made it a law that American colonists had to pay a tax on most every piece of paper used. (The paper used for licenses, documents, newspapers, magazines, etc., carried an official British stamp on it, and that's why it was called the Stamp Act.) Just imagine! What if it was required that you pay money for the use of each piece of paper in your notebook? The purpose of the money collected by the Stamp Act was to pay the British troops that were defending the American frontier. For the American colonists, the real controversy was the fact that the Parliament didn't seek the input from the American legislature. That is, the colonists didn't have a say in whether they were taxed or not.*
>
> *What would you do? Would you pay, or would you fight the tax?*

Creating a Comic Strip

Project-Based Writing Connection: Through illustrations and brief text, a comic strip or a page from a graphic novel can highlight the most important points of the narrative.

You can take inspiration from the look of comic books and graphic novels in order to add a fresh visual element to a text-heavy project. These formats perfectly combine visual elements with writing, and they offer a great way to illustrate the main idea (or the most suspenseful part) of a narrative.

The comic strip below is an example of a way to illustrate a key moment in the poem "The Midnight Ride of Paul Revere."

By illustrating these moments from this poem in frames, the artist is showing what he or she believes to be the most important part of the poem. This guides the reader/viewer to a more complete understanding of the poem.

He springs to the saddle, the bridle he turns,
But lingers and gazes, till full on his sight
A second lamp in the belfry burns!

Teacher Note: Distribute copies of the comic-strip template on page 45 for your students. Have them read and follow the directions on that page.

21st-Century Connection: You may also choose to use an online comic-strip program. Try one of the following, which are free:

❖ *http://www.makebeliefscomix.com/Comix/*

❖ *http://www.readwritethink.org/files/resources/interactives/comic/*

❖ *http://www.stripcreator.com/make.php*

There are other comic programs that provide more creative control to the user but may not be free. An example would be Comic Life (available through the Apple iLife suite), which allows users to convert photos into comic-book-like illustrations and provides numerous templates featuring varying layouts.

Creating a Comic Strip *(cont.)*

Directions: Use the template below to create frames for a comic strip based on your topic. First, you have to decide what are the most important elements of the story or argument to draw. Then, you have to decide on the visual style of your drawing.

Here is a list of elements to focus on:

Story Elements	Writing Devices	Camera Angles
❖ plot	❖ hook	❖ close-ups
❖ setting	❖ sequence	❖ ¾ shots
❖ characters	❖ suspense	❖ long shots
❖ descriptions	❖ foreshadowing	❖ foreground vs. background
❖ conflict	❖ zooming in on a moment	
❖ resolution	❖ dialogue	
❖ theme		

Making a Flip Book

 Project-Based Writing Connection: A flip book can be the perfect way to show — both textually and visually — a sequence of steps or events.

A flip book is a mini project in itself that includes both writing and art in order to describe a sequence of steps or events. These steps can form a how-to description, a summary of a novel, a chronological timeline, or even a scientific guide through a particular process. The different pages of the flip book can also be used to illustrate the different elements of a complex issue.

In order to make a flip book, you need these materials:

- ❖ several sheets of paper
- ❖ stapler
- ❖ drawing supplies
- ❖ pen

Then, follow these steps:

1. Stagger several sheets of paper in order to create visible tabs.
2. Next, fold the sheets to create a booklet of consistently spaced tabs.
3. Staple the booklet's folded edge.
4. On the cover, give your flip book a title (the name of the book, the name of the process being described, etc.). Also write your name.
5. Label the tabs by section or chapter.
6. Fill in your summaries, responses, and art.

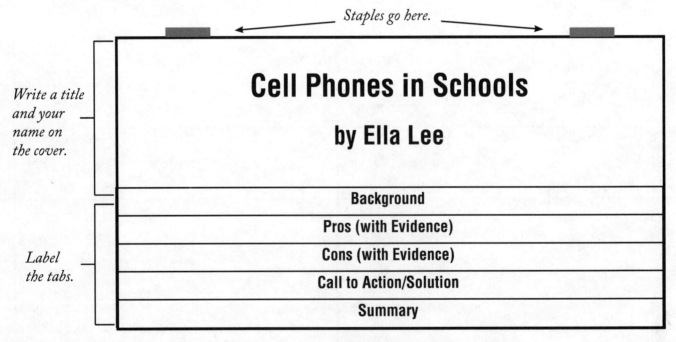

Teacher Note: Students can also go online to create a flip book at the following site: *http://www.readwritethink.org/files/resources/interactives/flipbook/.*

Wrapping It All Up

> **Project-Based Writing Connection:** A container provides an attractive way to present your final project visually, while also tying all of its individual elements together.

Finding a visual way to present your project is important when getting ready to turn in the final results. The package or container in which you house your work is another opportunity to show what you know. It's like the punctuation at the end of the sentence or the glue that holds it all together. It's a visual way to really send home your message with your audience.

Directions: In the activity below, draw lines to match the container with its appropriate topic. The first one has been done for you.

Pizza Box with essays inserted inside	**Pollution**
Clothes Hanger with essays dangling below at different levels	**Body Image**
Globe with a collage of essays taped onto its surface	**Childhood Obesity**
Rolled Scrolls tied together with a ribbon and quill	**Ocean Levels**
Trash-Can Lid with essays glued to the inside	**The History of the Amendments**

Now, what containers would you pick for the following topics?

1. Protecting endangered species _____

2. Global warming _____

3. Cell phones in schools _____

4. Getting rid of the Post Office _____

5. Library closures _____

Ask Yourself: What container could you use to house your own project? How is that container a symbol of your project, and how does it help your audience connect with your topic?

Cornell Notes

Project-Based Writing Connection: This resource can help you organize and process information for any project.

Cornell notes are a great way to organize your researched information. You use Cornell notes to . . .

❖ **Record key points.** This helps you think of the overall concepts.

❖ **Make detailed notes.** This helps you dig deeper into the key points.

❖ **Write a reflective summary.** This can help embed the information more deeply into your memory.

A page of Cornell notes is divided into three main sections:

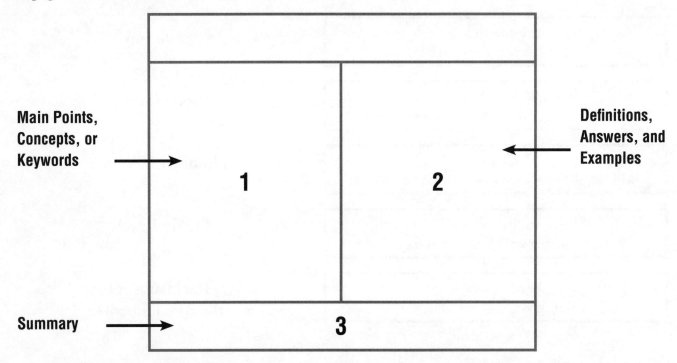

1. **Main Points, Concepts, or Keywords** — This information should be recorded in the left-hand column on the page. Main ideas and key elements (dates, people, etc.) should be included here. You may also use this space to develop questions that need to be answered about the topic.

2. **Definitions, Answers, and Examples** — This information should be recorded in the right-hand column. Use this large space to explain the terms and answer the questions listed on the left. Be brief and clear. Do this by using bullets or short phrases and skipping lines between ideas.

3. **Summary** — A brief summary of the topic and your finding should be recorded here. Aim to summarize the information in three sentences or less.

Reminder: Don't forget to put such information as your name, the date, and your topic along the top of your page of Cornell notes.

You can use these instructions to create your own Cornell notes on a piece of lined paper, or you can use the blank template provided on page 49.

Cornell Notes *(cont.)*

Directions: Use this template to help organize your research about your topic.

Name:	Date:
Topic:	Class:

Main Points, Concepts, or Keywords:	Definitions, Answers, and Examples:

Summary:

Bibliographies

Project-Based Writing Connection: This resource shows you how to cite the different types of information used in research projects. (Blank templates are included on page 51.)

Every research essay needs evidence, and every piece of evidence came from somewhere. It's important, therefore, to learn how to create a proper bibliography. Keep the following resource on hand for your bibliographical reference needs.

Bibliography Cheat Sheet

Book

Author's last name, first name. *Book title.* City of publication: Publishing company, Publication date. Pages. Medium.

Example:

Collins, Suzanne. *The Hunger Games.* New York: Scholastic Press, 2008. 12–23. Print.

Article in a Newspaper or Magazine

Author's last name, first name. "Article title." *Periodical title.* Month, Year: Pages of actual article. Medium.

Example:

Smith, John. "Dancing with the Cars." *Car and Driver Monthly.* April, 2003: 12–14. Print.

Website

"Name of page." *Name of website.* Editor(s) (if available). Date of publication or of the latest update (day/month/year). Medium. Date of access (days/month/year).

Example:

"Book Review: The Hunger Games." *Tweenteacher.* Wolpert-Gawron, Heather. 9 December 2008. Web. 7 March 2012.

Interview

Subject's last name, first name. Personal Interview. Date of interview (day, month, year).

Example:

Spielberg, Steven. Personal Interview. 14 January 2011.

Movie

Title. Name of director. Year of release. Format. Studio, release date of format.

Example:

E.T: The Extraterrestrial. Steven Spielberg. 1982. DVD. Universal Studios, 2005.

21st-Century Connection: The website *www.easybib.com* is a free, automatic bibliography-entry creator. Just type in the information, and it puts it into the correct format. But be prepared: you need to know what information to enter, or your bibliography will be incomplete!

Bibliographies *(cont.)*

Directions: Use these forms to record the correct information as you gather research. You may not be able to fill in every line, depending on the type of resource and the information provided.

Information Source: Book

Author's Name: _____

Title of Book or Selection: _____

Series Title: _____

Editor or Translator's Name: _____

Edition and Volume Number: _____

Publisher: _____

Publication City and Date: _____

Page Numbers: _____

Comments: _____

Information Source: Periodical (magazine, newspaper, etc.)

Author's Name: _____

Title of Article: _____

Title of Periodical: _____

Series and Volume Numbers: _____

Publication Date: _____

Page Numbers: _____

Comments: _____

Information Source: Internet

Author's Name: _____

Title of Article or Page: _____

Name of Website or Company: _____

URL: _____

Publication Date (or Date Last Revised): _____

Access Date: _____

Comments: _____

Outline — Narrative/Story

Project-Based Writing Connection: This resource can help you flesh out narratives, and it can also help keep you focused on what you need to do to successfully complete a task.

A *narrative/story* is a piece of writing or speech that describes a sequence of events. A narrative can be completely fictional (like a fantasy) or based on truth to some degree. It includes any kind of story — from science fiction to love stories to personal memoirs.

Here are some elements to look for when reading and revising narratives:

I. The Opening (Exposition)
- **A.** Hook
- **B.** Characters
    - 1. Physical Traits
    - 2. Personality Traits
- **C.** Setting
- **D.** Main Story Conflict

II. The Body (Rising Action — Climax — Falling Action)
- **A.** Sequential Events (or flashback if using that strategy)
- **B.** Sensory or Emotion Details (sight, smell, touch, taste, hear, feel in your heart)
- **C.** Foreshadowing/Suspense
- **D.** Figurative Language (simile, metaphor, onomatopoeia, personification, etc.)
- **E.** Dialogue
- **F.** Description of Facial Expression, Gestures
- **G.** Transitions
- **H.** Action Verbs

III. The Ending (Resolution)
- **A.** "Tie it all up"
- **B.** Lesson Learned, Theme, Moral, Motto, etc.

Hint! Remember to incorporate these six traits of good writing for added sophistication:

- ❏ Sentence Variety
- ❏ Proper Conventions
- ❏ Great Ideas
- ❏ Voice
- ❏ Word Choice
- ❏ Organization

Outline — Narrative/Story *(cont.)*

Project-Based Writing Connection: This resource provides a visual way to look at story structure. Use it to map out stories.

Directions: Use the story swoop to organize your narrative. Write the most important parts of your story in the appropriate places along the swoop. This will illustrate how your narrative flows from one idea to the next.

The Story Swoop

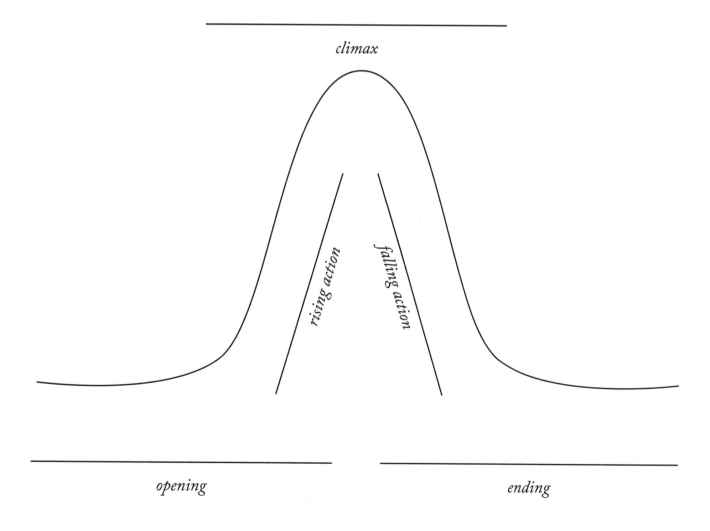

Outline — Persuasive

Project-Based Writing Connection: This resource can help you craft a piece of writing that will effectively persuade your reader to view a topic from your perspective.

The terms *advocacy* and *persuasive* refer to writing that is meant to influence and change minds. Being able to write a successful **persuasive** essay is an important skill. Use the strongest word choices and evidence in order to increase your chances of convincing your readers.

Here are some elements to look for when reading and revising persuasive writing:

I. Introduction
- **A.** Hook
- **B.** Background information
- **C.** Who is affected by this issue?
- **D.** Thesis Statement (Opinion + Reason #1 + Reason #2)
   For instance: *I strongly believe that the school vending machines should only sell water because it is a healthy alternative to sugary drinks and it is less expensive to buy.*

II. Body paragraph: Reason #1
- **A.** Main Topic Sentence (general statement)
- **B.** Expansion of the Main Topic (gets more specific)
- **C.** Textual Evidence/Proof (quotes, statistics, data, personal experience, etc.)
- **D.** Commentary/Connection to the evidence
- **E.** Transition to next paragraph

III. Body paragraph: Reason #2
- **A.** Main Topic Sentence (general statement)
- **B.** Expansion of the Main Topic (gets more specific)
- **C.** Textual Evidence/Proof (quotes, statistics, data, personal experience, etc.)
- **D.** Commentary/Connection to the evidence
- **E.** Transition to next paragraph

IV. Counterargument
- **A.** Main Topic Sentence (states the opposing side's *best* point)
- **B.** Expansion of the Main Topic (gets more specific)
- **C.** Textual Evidence/Proof (quotes, statistics, data, personal experience, etc.)
- **D.** Commentary/Connection to the evidence
- **E.** Conclusion that *refutes* this point (i.e., why it doesn't convince you)

V. Conclusion
- **A.** Reiterate Thesis (using different words)
- **B.** Solution/Call to Action (what we should do about it)

Outline — Summary

 Project-Based Writing Connection: This resource can help you focus on only the most important parts of a piece of writing.

A **summary** is the gist of a more complex piece of writing. It is meant to educate readers quickly by giving an overview of the most important points. The key is to make it simple so that anyone can understand the issue.

Here are some points to remember when writing a summary:

✔ Don't give your opinion.

✔ Stick to the facts in the original piece.

✔ Select the most important points and disregard points that aren't important.

A rough outline could be as follows:

I. Main Topic Sentence
   A. Include the writing's TAG (title, author, and genre — if it applies).
   B. Keep this sentence general.

II. Most Ideas
   A. Only use the most important points.
   B. Disregard small details.
   C. Use transitions.
   D. Go in chronological order.
   E. Don't use voice.
   F. Use sentence variety.

III. Conclusion
   A. Don't simply give your opinion!

Outline — Response to Literature

 Project-Based Writing Connection: This resource can help you get organized when you write about another piece of writing, such as a novel, story, essay, or poem.

A *response-to-literature essay* is a chance to weigh in on something you have read. There are a few different ways to write a response to literature.

❖ You can come up with a theory about what or how the author was trying to communicate.

❖ You can relate the writing to real life or the time in which it was written.

❖ You can explain your personal response to the writing.

Make sure you know what type of response-to-literature essay your teacher is looking for. No matter what type you write, though, it is important to support your statements with quotations from the literature and explain the quotations.

A rough outline could be as follows:

I. Introduction
   A. Hook
   B. Background information (what you are responding to, who wrote it, what type of text it is)
   C. Thesis statement

II. Body Paragraphs
   A. Reasons supporting your thesis (one per paragraph)
   B. Quotations that illustrate your reasons
   C. Explanations of what each quotation means and how it supports your point
   D. Graceful transitions

III. Conclusion
   A. Thesis statement reiterated and explained
   B. Implications/parting thoughts

The Writing-Genre Matrix

 Project-Based Writing Connection: This resource can get you thinking about the structure, purpose, and content of different forms of writing. This helps you choose the best genre(s) for your purpose when writing.

Directions: Study the matrix below, which shows the various elements that go into five different genres of writing: Narrative, Summary, Argument (Persuasive), Response to Literature, and Informational.

Teacher Note: This chart is meant to get students thinking about the overlap in writing genres. The categorization of these elements may be up for debate. For instance, it could be said that "voice" can be found in many genres. Use this resource to spark a classroom discussion about writing.

Genre	Narrative	Summary	Argument	Response	Informational
Hook	√		√	√	
Background Info	√		√	√	√
Thesis Statement			√	√	√
TAG (title/author/genre)		√		√	
Main Topic Sentence		√	√	√	√
Evidence			√	√	√
Commentary			√	√	√
Transition Words	√	√	√	√	√
Voice	√				
Sentence Variety	√	√	√	√	√
Conventions	√	√	√	√	√
Figurative Language	√				
Plot	√				
Rising Action	√				
Exposition	√				
Setting	√				
Characters	√				
Conflict	√		√		
Falling Action	√				
Resolution	√				
Theme	√	√			
Counterargument			√		
Call to Action/Solution			√		

Unit Checklist

Project-Based Writing Connection: A checklist can help you organize your time and your work so that you never lose sight of your deadlines.

Tips for Using this Checklist

❖ In the "Assigned Element" column, fill in a more general type of element, like "Research" or "Written Piece" or "Visual Element."

❖ Use the "Possibilities" column to brainstorm possible ways you could fulfill those requirements, such as "Survey" for research or "Movie Poster" for visual element. Really try to jot down a lot of ideas in the "Possibilities" column.

Date Due	Date Done	Assigned Element	Possibilities

Using Rubrics

 Project-Based Writing Connection: Rubrics can help you understand what is expected of you before you begin each element of a project.

Rubrics are important because they serve two vital purposes:

1. Rubrics tell a student how he or she did.

2. By clearly defining your expectations to students, rubrics serve as preemptive feedback.

Over the next few pages, several rubrics are featured. They fall into two categories:

teacher-created   **student-created**

Both can be used peer-to-peer to evaluate student rough drafts, or they can be used to evaluate a final project itself.

If completed prior to producing the actual project, a student-created rubric can really motivate students by driving home what is necessary to achieve the highest score possible.

Before handing out the student-created rubric worksheet on page 61, distribute copies of the following card to students. It can serve as a step-by-step "How To" guide for students to follow as they create their rubrics.

Creating a Rubric

Creating a rubric for an element of a project (a narrative, an oral presentation, an expository paper, a visual, etc.) is simple. It just takes three basic steps:

Step 1: <u>In the left-hand column</u>, list the qualities that you believe are the most important in order to do well on the project.

Step 2: <u>Across the top</u>, list the rankings that would describe how well a person did. Do this by writing a number and a word. For instance, you could write "4 – Fantastic" in the first box, and you could write "1 – Poor" in the last box.

Step 3: <u>In the boxes of the matrix</u>, write descriptions of what the various scores would look like. Use words that you know.

Using Rubrics *(cont.)*

Teacher-Created Rubrics

Below are different possible rubric templates that can be used with various projects.

Project Rubric

Criteria	Exceeds	Meets	Approaching	Not Evident
Research Quality				
Theme Appears Throughout				
Quality of Writing				
Creativity				
Neatness				
Organization				
Bibliography				
Conventions				
Presentation				

Oral-Presentation Rubric

Criteria	3	2	1
Volume			
Stance			
Eye Contact			
Information Quality			
Intonation			
Speed			

Using Rubrics *(cont.)*

Student-Created Rubrics

Reading a teacher-created rubric is really helpful, but a more powerful way to use rubrics is to create one yourself to evaluate your own project or a peer's project. If you have a hand in designing your own rubric, it helps you to understand more of what to expect!

Directions: Look at this sample rubric. How would you translate it into your own words? What does a "4" mean? What do the words mean to you? In the blank template below, use your own words to re-create the rubric.

Sample	4	3	2	1
Quality of Writing	Sentences are exceedingly coherent. The standards are exceeded.	Sentences are coherent. Standards are met.	Sentences are simple in nature and almost meet the standards.	Sentences are incomplete and in fragments. There are few or no complete sentences.
Ideas and Concepts	There is a high level of critical-thinking in the ideas and concepts.	The level of thinking in the ideas and concepts is acceptable.	The ideas and concepts are approaching acceptability. They still indicate a lack of awareness of the content-matter.	The ideas are simple and do not indicate grade-level thinking.

Create Your Own Rubric

Teacher Feedback

 Project-Based Writing Connection: Getting one-on-one conference time with the teacher can help you focus on what you are doing right and what you need to work on.

At times, you might need help with some aspect of your project. Often, a quick conference with your teacher will do just the trick. Be prepared to make the most out of the opportunity to receive such helpful feedback.

Take the form below with you to your conference. Take notes as your teacher talks; this will help you absorb the information more fully. You can use these notes later as a reference when you are revising or finalizing your paper.

Teacher Note: You might not need to fill in every line of this form. Just use it as a guide.

Own Your Own Feedback

Notes on Your Topic/Theme: _____

_____

_____

Notes on Your Thesis Statement: _____

_____

_____

This is great: Keep doing it, don't change a thing! (List skills you've done well.)

_____

_____

This could be better: Reconsider, mull over, overhaul. (List items you still need to work on.)

_____

_____

Based on the work in front of me today, my teacher is giving me a(n) _____.

(*enter grade*)

Think about it: Am I satisfied with that grade?   Yes   No

Due date of final draft, based on our discussion: _____

Signed: _____   Date: _____

Unit 1: Teach the Teacher

Teacher Instructions

 It can be said that those who are teaching are also learning, so why not ask the students to teach? After all, knowing content is important, but being able to communicate that content is even more so. And let's face it, what student doesn't want to be the authority somehow? This unit gives them the opportunity to do just that.

"Teach the Teacher" is a multi-genre unit that asks each student to select a topic for a course that he or she will teach to the class in a way that engages all of the different learners in the class. While that goal can be really hard to accomplish (as any teacher will tell you), students will learn a lot in the attempt to achieve it.

This unit is all about the power of student choice. It puts the authority of the lesson in the students' hands, scaffolding each lesson step by step until each student is ready to present an entire lesson and assessment to the whole class.

This unit includes the following components:

❖ **"Teachable Topics"** (page 64) — Begin the unit by distributing this worksheet. Use it to guide students in choosing topics that will be both fun and rigorous to research and teach.

❖ **"How Learners Learn"** (pages 65–66) — Introduce the concept of how different learners learn. Have students match up the learning categories with various activities, which will help them think about how their topics can be taught in ways that reach different learners.

❖ **"Pitch Your Topic"** (page 67) — Have students research and pitch in writing their topics to you, the teacher.

❖ **"Create a Lesson Plan"** (pages 68–69) — Show an example of a lesson plan for teaching a topic, and then have students create outlines for their own lesson plans.

❖ **"Quiz the Class"** (pages 70–71) — Examine the different types of quiz questions before having students create quizzes based on their teaching topics. (Note: Before distributing these pages, locate an appropriate quiz-making website. Sign up for an account, if needed, so that your students can use the website to create quizzes online.)

❖ **"Give an Oral Presentation"** (pages 72–74) — Give students tips on the why's and how's of planning a successful oral presentation, which they will then use to present their topics to the class.

❖ **"Write a Persuasive Letter"** (page 75) — Direct students to write a business letter to a school administrator; this letter will explain why their topic should be considered as a possible new elective for the following school year.

❖ **"Unit Checklist"** (page 76) — Provide students with this valuable resource, which will help them stay focused, on task, and in front of deadlines.

Teachable Topics

Finally, the time has come for you to teach the teacher (and all of the other students in your class). Has there ever been a topic that made you think, "Why don't they teach that in school?" Throughout the course of this unit, you will get the chance not only to teach this topic, but also to persuade your teacher and your school administrator that this topic should be taught over and over again—by you, of course.

Now the question remains: What will you choose to teach everyone about? Your topic can be anything from "The History of . . ." (the Olympics, the Toaster, the Internet, etc.) to "How to . . ." (prepare a Caesar salad, throw a curveball, master a particular video game, etc.). The possibilities are endless.

Choose a topic with which you are familiar but about which you can learn more through research. After all, the more knowledge and insight you can bring to this topic, the better chance you will have to convince everyone that it is a subject worth teaching.

Directions: Think of three possible topics for you to teach. List the pros and cons of teaching each topic. "Pros" may be how much you know about the topic, how interesting you think it will be for others to learn, etc. "Cons" may be that it would be difficult for others to learn, the cost or availability of materials needed to teach the class, etc.

Possible Topic #1 _____

    Pros: _____   Cons: _____

    _____   _____

    _____   _____

Possible Topic #2 _____

    Pros: _____   Cons: _____

    _____   _____

    _____   _____

Possible Topic #3 _____

    Pros: _____   Cons: _____

    _____   _____

    _____   _____

Now look back at your three possible topics. It's time to make your choice. Which will it be?

My Chosen Topic → ⟨_____⟩

How Learners Learn

Knowing the different ways in which people learn helps a teacher design lessons that are interesting to lots of students. There are seven learning categories to consider, and a teacher needs to be able to recognize them all in order to create effective lessons. Here are brief descriptions of each category.

❖ **Interpersonal:** uses a deep understanding of oneself; is reflective

❖ **Kinesthetic:** uses sports and movement

❖ **Linguistic:** uses language (words, writing)

❖ **Logical:** uses science and math (numbers, charts, and graphs)

❖ **Musical:** uses tone and rhythm

❖ **Natural:** uses a knowledge and appreciation of nature and the world beyond oneself

❖ **Visual:** uses art, design, and shapes

Directions: In the boxes below, create symbols to represent each learning category. For instance, for Linguistic, you might draw a quill pen to represent writing.

Interpersonal	**Kinesthetic**	**Linguistic**

Logical	**Musical**	**Natural**	**Visual**

Now think about ways you can meet the different styles of learning as you design lessons for your chosen topic. This will make it more likely that all students are interested in the activities that you are teaching. Jot down some of your ideas on the lines below, and then complete the activity on the next page.

_____

_____

_____

_____

How Learners Learn *(cont.)*

Directions: Look at the examples of activities below. Match the kind of learning to the activity. Do this by drawing in the box the symbol you created on the previous page. If you think more than one kind of learning applies, draw multiple symbols.

As the teacher, you ask your students to . . .

1. Write an original song about a topic. **Symbol(s):**	**5.** Create a time line of events for the history of your topic. **Symbol(s):**
2. Play charades in small groups to act out vocabulary. **Symbol(s):**	**6.** Give a short speech about how the topic can apply to their lives outside of school. **Symbol(s):**
3. Write a diary entry from the point of view of an historical figure associated with your topic. **Symbol(s):**	**7.** Create and perform a dance that illustrates the topic. **Symbol(s):**
4. Design a poster to advertise for your topic. **Symbol(s):**	**8.** Write a journal entry about how your topic may have come to be a part of our world in the first place. **Symbol(s):**

- -

Teacher Note: Fold this section under to cover it before making copies.

Possible answers: **1.** musical; **2.** kinesthetic; **3.** linguistic; **4.** visual; **5.** logical; **6.** interpersonal; **7.** musical, kinesthetic; **8.** linguistic, natural

Pitch Your Topic

Regardless of your topic, it's always vital to get it approved first by your teacher. For your next assignment, you will create a well-written, convincing pitch to help your teacher see why your topic is not only an important one to research, but one that, based on your interest-level, would get the highest quality of work out of you.

Directions: Use the following outline to help you brainstorm and plan out the elements of an essay about your topic. Use the results to write your persuasive pitch on a separate piece of paper.

I. **Hook** — Begin your essay with a sentence that will grab your teacher's attention.

   Ideas and Notes: _____

   _____

II. **Background Information** — Pretend your teacher knows nothing about this topic. Write one or two sentences to give him or her the gist of the subject you want to research further.

   Ideas and Notes: _____

   _____

III. **Thesis Statement** — Try to write one sophisticated statement that says what you want to study and why. Use the following format:

   I want to be permitted to research _____ *because* _____.

   Give two reasons why this topic is fascinating to you.

   Ideas and Notes: _____

   _____

   _____

IV. **Counterargument** — Give a one-sentence counterargument that acknowledges why your teacher might be skeptical of allowing you to spend time researching your topic.

   Ideas and Notes: _____

   _____

V. **Your Response** — Refute this counterargument. That is, counter the counterargument. Write one sentence that speaks directly to your teacher's concerns and convinces him or her why you should still be permitted to continue with your subject.

   Ideas and Notes: _____

   _____

Create a Lesson Plan

In order to engage learners, you need a plan. Many teachers design formal lessons plans for each lesson in order to break down how to best communicate their content to the class. You will now do the same.

The plan you will be creating should include the following elements:

❖ **Objective** — What is the specific skill that you want your class to know? What is the broader lesson that you will be teaching?

❖ **Materials** — List the things you will need to conduct your lesson. This is not only for you, but also for your teacher so he or she can provide you with the items.

❖ **Step-by-Step Lesson** — Give some thought to what you will do first, second, third, etc., as you walk through the lesson.

❖ **Check for Understanding** — Develop some questions to ask students as you progress through your lesson to make sure that they are "with you."

❖ **Assessment** — Create and distribute a quiz to assess how well your students listened, as well as how effectively you presented your material.

Here is a sample lesson plan that follows this outline:

Objective: I want my class to learn how to create California rolls and learn about how Japanese cuisine is influenced by that country's geography.

Materials:

❖ rice	❖ ginger	❖ table
❖ rice vinegar	❖ wasabi	❖ document camera
❖ crab	❖ soy sauce	❖ LCD projector
❖ avocado	❖ pre-made CA rolls	❖ map of Japan
❖ cucumber	❖ bamboo rolling pad	❖ Cornell notes
❖ seaweed	❖ knife	

Step-by-Step Lesson: 1. Introduce materials. **2.** Discuss Japanese geography. Ask students to predict what foods are eaten in Japan, based on its location and land. **3.** Lay out bamboo pad and seaweed under the document camera. **4.** Add crab, avocado, and cucumber. **5.** Roll ingredients. **6.** Cut roll into six pieces. **7.** Take out pre-made rolls from a container and distribute one piece to each student. (Mention food allergies.)

Check for Understanding:

1. "What alternative could you suggest instead of using crab?"

2. "Just to review: Why is fish such a large part of the Japanese diet?"

3. "Could someone remind us of the first three steps to make a California roll?"

Assessment: Distribute a 10-question quiz to students.

Create a Lesson Plan *(cont.)*

It is your turn to create a lesson plan that will help you teach your topic to the class.

Directions: Follow the outline below to create a rough draft of your lesson plan.

Objective: _____

_____

Materials:

Step-by-Step Lesson (only fill in as many steps as are needed):

Step 1: _____

Step 2: _____

Step 3: _____

Step 4: _____

Step 5: _____

Step 6: _____

Step 7: _____

Step 8: _____

Check for Understanding:

1. _____

2. _____

3. _____

Assessment: _____

Quiz the Class

Developing excellent, high-level questions is a great way to assess your own knowledge of a subject. It's also a perfect way to assess if someone understood what you taught or what you produced.

You are going to develop a 10-question quiz on your topic using a variety of different formats of questions. After all, it gets boring for your peers to take a quiz that is delivered in just one format.

Here are three different kinds of questions to include in your quizzes:

❖ A **forced-choice** question is one that "forces" the test-takers to settle on an answer that the test-creator previously determined.

   Examples of forced-choice questions: Multiple Choice, True/False, Matching

❖ A **rank-order** question is one that asks an opinion of the test-taker, but it still must be given within a set range.

   Examples of rank-order questions: Star Rating ("1 star" for worst, "5 stars" for best), Assigning a Letter Grade ("A" for best, "B" for next best, etc.)

❖ An **open-ended** question is one that gives the authority to the test-taker, allowing him or her to determine the answer.

   Examples of open-ended questions: Short Answer, Essay Response

Directions: On a separate piece of paper, create your own quiz based on your lesson presentation. It should be made up of the following types of questions:

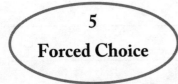
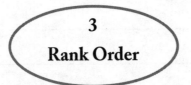
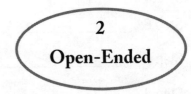

When you are creating your own quiz, you should take inspiration from the assessments you've taken as a student. Which kinds of question do you believe really challenge you to remember the material? Which kinds of question are the most engaging?

21st-Century Connection: Go online to a quiz-making website that your teacher has chosen. There, you can design a quiz using the different methods above. Have your classmates take the test, and the website will score and assess the results.

Quiz the Class *(cont.)*

In the following activity, look at the questions and decide if they are **Forced Choice**, **Rank Order**, or **Open-Ended**. Then, explain your answer. The first one has been done for you.

Hint: Only answer the "What type of question is it?" and the "Why?" questions.

Question #1. Should vending machines with soda and candy be allowed in schools?
- ❑ Yes, kids have the right to choose what they eat and drink.
- ❑ No, school vending machines should be filled with healthy drinks and snacks.

What type of question is it? _____Forced Choice_____ **Why?** <u>I am only given the two choices</u>
<u>written by the author; therefore, I'm forced to choose between the two.</u>

Question #2. How should my school handle the long lunch lines? Rank the following from 1 to 4 ("1" being best and "4" being worst).
- _____ Stagger lunch times.
- _____ Create cards that earn "front of the line" privileges.
- _____ Create new open-server windows.
- _____ Sell food in carts outside the cafeteria, as well as from the cafeteria itself.

What type of question is it? _____ **Why?** _____
_____

Question #3. What prevention efforts are needed to help young people dealing with eating disorders?

What type of question is it? _____ **Why?** _____
_____

Question #4. Which statement best describes your attitude toward global warming?
- **A.** I don't think it will happen.
- **B.** People and governments should act now to try to prevent or prepare for it.
- **C.** The world may change, but living creatures will adapt.
- **D.** There's nothing we can do about it.

What type of question is it? _____ **Why?** _____
_____

Question #5. What can we do when the gas prices are high?

What type of question is it? _____ **Why?** _____
_____

- -

Teacher Note: Fold this section under to cover it before making copies.

Answers: **2.** Rank Order; **3.** Open-Ended; **4.** Forced Choice; **5.** Open-Ended

Give an Oral Presentation

Great speakers don't just wing it and hope for the best. They know where they are going to start and where they are going to end. They also have an idea of how long it will take to get there. To do that, you should have an outline (not a full script) of what you're going to say.

Directions: It is time to present your topic to the class. In minutes, you will need to be able to explain why your topic would make for a valuable school subject that should be taught. Use the next few pages to assist you in completing this task.

❖ On this page, you will find a helpful "Presentation Reminders" card that you can use on the day of your speech to help keep you focused and on track.

❖ On the next page, you will find many tips to help you time your presentation.

❖ On the third page, you will find a template for your presentation.

Begin by writing an outline of your presentation. Base this outline on the lesson plan you have already created. Once you've written your outline, then the real rehearsals begin. When you practice your oral presentation, you need to be aware of multiple elements. Cut out the reminder card below. Use it to help you practice your speech. You can also bring it up to the front of the class with you and put it where you can see it as you present. This will help remind you of what you need to be aware of as you speak in front of an audience.

Presentation Reminders

Volume

Can your audience (your *whole* audience) hear you? Remember to **speak loudly** enough so that the person at the back of the room can hear you.

Emphasis

Are your words flat and monotone, or is there emotion in your voice? How many "um"s, "er"s, or moments of silence are there in your presentation? Are you mumbling? Remember to **speak clearly** and show emotion.

Stance

Are you leaning, fidgeting, or rocking? Remember to **stand up straight**.

Eye Contact

Are you connecting with your audience with your eyes? Or are your eyes trapped to your cue cards and notes? Remember to **look at people** in different parts of the room.

Content

Did you do your research and are you communicating that research? Remember to **stay on topic**.

Timing

Are you speeding? Remember to **speak as if you're telling a story**.

Give an Oral Presentation *(cont.)*

The issue of timing is an important one when you are speaking in front of an audience. It takes rehearsing your oral presentation over and over — in front of a mirror, for your family, maybe for your friends.

If you were to write an entire speech out on an 8½" x 11" piece of paper, the general rule of thumb is as follows:

1 minute of speech = about ¾ of a page of handwriting

So think about it. If you were doing a 3-minute presentation, you would be writing about a 4-page monologue. (If 3 = ¾ times x, then x = 4.) The challenge, however, is to actually become so familiar with your speech that you don't need to memorize a totally written essay. Instead, write an outline, and see if you can hit the beats again and again so that your presentation times out right every time you practice.

Directions: Below is an activity that will aid you in timing out your presentation perfectly. Follow the steps provided.

Step 1

Create an outline of your content. Base this outline on your lesson plan.

Step 2

Grab a timer.

Step 3

Stand up and use this worksheet as a cheat sheet as you time your presentation one section at a time.

Step 4

Slow down! Don't be nervous, and be sure to stay in control of your speed rather than the speed being in control of you. It might feel weird, but do it in slow motion once all the way through. Then try it again at a normal pace. This will help you avoid going too fast.

Step 5

With each attempt, write down your time next to the section to indicate your speed and pacing. Get it consistent, and you're ready to go.

Step 6

Repeat. Do it over and over until you don't need the timer to tell you how long you are spending on each section.

Give an Oral Presentation *(cont.)*

Directions: Below is one possible oral presentation broken down into sections. Chunk your presentation into sections, and time each section using the template below.

Hook

    1st time through: _____   3rd time through: _____

    2nd time through: _____   4th time through: _____

Did you slow down with each rehearsal? Circle your response.   **YES**   **NO**

Background Information

    1st time through: _____   3rd time through: _____

    2nd time through: _____   4th time through: _____

Did you slow down with each rehearsal? Circle your response.   **YES**   **NO**

Main Content

    1st time through: _____   3rd time through: _____

    2nd time through: _____   4th time through: _____

Did you slow down with each rehearsal? Circle your response.   **YES**   **NO**

Questions & Answers (practice with someone asking you questions and you responding)

    1st time through: _____   3rd time through: _____

    2nd time through: _____   4th time through: _____

Did you slow down with each rehearsal? Circle your response.   **YES**   **NO**

Administer Quiz (Giving instructions)

    1st time through: _____   3rd time through: _____

    2nd time through: _____   4th time through: _____

Did you slow down with each rehearsal? Circle your response.   **YES**   **NO**

At the end of each full presentation, add your totals together to see how well you're timing it.

    1st time through: _____   3rd time through: _____

    2nd time through: _____   4th time through: _____

Reflection

    ❖ Which was your best time?_____

    ❖ Why do you think it went better than the other times?_____

_____

Write a Persuasive Letter

One of the most important elements to include in a "Teach the Teacher" unit is a persuasive business letter to a school administrator. Remember, the point of all of your research, writing, and lesson planning has been to develop an imaginary elective for the next school year. Now you just have to put all those skills together.

Directions: On a separate piece of paper, write a persuasive letter in the form of a business letter. Do your best to convince an administrator that your topic would make for a worthwhile class. Remember your writing skills, remember your audience, and remember to be persuasive.

Follow the format below:

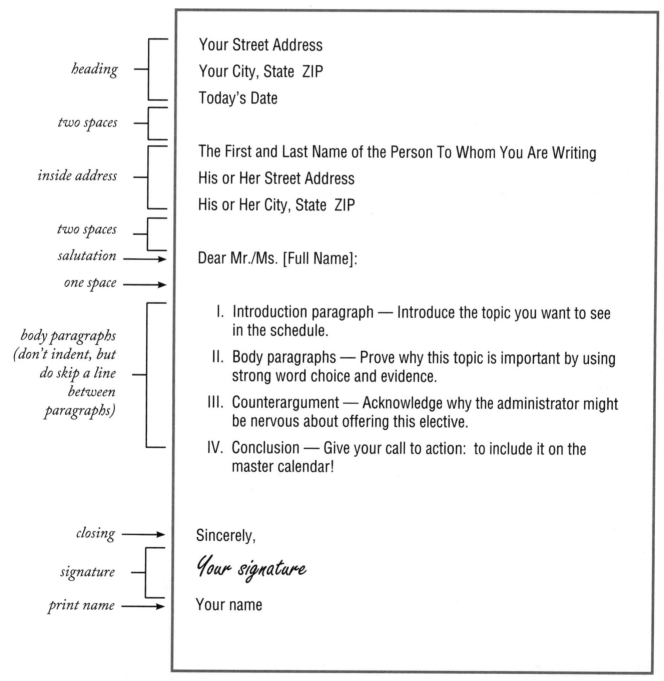

heading

Your Street Address

Your City, State ZIP

Today's Date

two spaces

The First and Last Name of the Person To Whom You Are Writing

inside address

His or Her Street Address

His or Her City, State ZIP

two spaces

salutation

Dear Mr./Ms. [Full Name]:

one space

body paragraphs (don't indent, but do skip a line between paragraphs)

I. Introduction paragraph — Introduce the topic you want to see in the schedule.

II. Body paragraphs — Prove why this topic is important by using strong word choice and evidence.

III. Counterargument — Acknowledge why the administrator might be nervous about offering this elective.

IV. Conclusion — Give your call to action: to include it on the master calendar!

closing

Sincerely,

signature

Your signature

print name

Your name

Unit Checklist

Below is a possible checklist for the "Teach the Teacher" unit. It should help to organize your time and work as you move through the process of creating a full project. Look ahead on your checklist and never lose sight of deadlines!

Genre	Description	Due	Turned In
1. Persuasive Writing	Write a persuasive business letter to your teacher pitching your topic.		
2. Lesson Plan	This is a step-by-step description of what you will teach, what you will need, and the activities that you will be doing with the class.		
3. Quiz	A 10-question assessment using various questioning strategies that the class will take and you will grade. (The score will not be counted against the students. You will score their quizzes as an assignment grade that goes toward your final score.)		
4. Bibliography	Include a works-cited page using correct bibliographical format.		
5. Oral Presentation	This will be scored using the oral-presentation rubric.		
6. Visual or Kinesthetic Element of Presentation	This can be an activity you are asking the students to do or a visual element used during your lesson plan (poster, PowerPoint, props, etc.).		
7. Your Choice	Choose an additional genre to depict your topic that will be turned in the day of your oral presentation along with the above requirements.		

Unit 2: Advocacy Research Project

Teacher Instructions

Advocacy is a future standard that caters specifically to connecting school life to real life. With the Advocacy Research Project, students choose a topic to study (and advocate for) and also the format in which they want to present their results. These topics should be based on current issues and should be ones that have an impact on the world around the students. After all, it doesn't matter if a student is in elementary school, he or she can still make an impact on the world.

This unit includes the following components:

❖ **"Zeroing In"** (pages 78–79) — Have students choose an advocacy topic that interests them. Along the way, they will consider the impact their topics have on the world around them. (Note: You may want to distribute three or more copies of the worksheet on page 78 to students so they can fill them out for multiple topics.)

❖ **"Write a Thesis Statement"** (pages 80–81) — Show how a thesis statement functions in a persuasive essay and have students create thesis statements for essays about their topics.

❖ **"The Newspaper Article"** (pages 82–83) — Examine the parts of a newspaper article and have students think about those elements in relation to their advocacy topics.

❖ **"Create a Graph"** (pages 84–85) — Discuss the functions of graphs, and examine two prevalent types (the bar graph and the pie chart).

❖ **"A Call to Action"** (page 86) — Offer several methods for students to choose from as they practice proposing solutions to advocacy topics.

❖ **"Unit Checklist"** (page 87) — Help students stay on task and in front of deadlines.

To begin, you first need to get your students comfortable with sifting through the news. Pick four students each week to bring in an article, blog post, etc., on topics that are important to them, their community, their country, etc. Collect the articles and keep them organized in a student-created resource library (see page 14). Then, once you are ready to begin the Advocacy Research Project, the students can begin the process of choosing topics by searching through what's already in the classroom. From there, have the students do the following:

Step 1 — After looking through the library, they should ask themselves these questions:

❖ Is there a topic out there that is newsworthy?

❖ Are there at least two sides to the issue?

❖ Can I find ample evidence to back up my opinion?

❖ Can I offer a solution or ask my reader/audience to do something to help the issue?

Step 2 — Write down a list of three possible topics they are interested in.

Step 3 — Once students choose their topics (see "Zeroing In"), they should maintain a bibliography based on where they conduct their research.

Zeroing In

Directions: It's time to choose a topic that is important and interesting to you. Fill out the following worksheet for a subject that you might want to focus on. Don't worry at this point about research, you're just trying to commit to a topic that you can enjoy learning about.

Topic: ⬡ _____ ⬡

List three facts you already know about this topic:

1. _____
2. _____
3. _____

Now, tease the topic out even further by listing one PRO and one CON for the issue:

Pro: _____

Con: _____

Next, answer the following questions about this topic:

1. Why is this topic important? _____
   _____

2. Why are you interested in this topic? How do you think you relate to it?
   _____
   _____

3. Why do you think it's important for your audience to learn about this topic?
   _____
   _____

Finally, think about researching this topic. Where will you go to find your information?

Check off the resource(s) you believe you will use. Don't worry, you're not committed yet. In fact, as you research, you'll find that your list of resources will grow. One will lead you to another.

❑ Books	❑ Websites	❑ Podcasts
❑ Interviews	❑ Videos	

21st-Century Connection: When you use Google to browse information, don't forget the Google Advanced Search. Advanced Search allows you to search magazines, scholarly articles, blogs, newsfeeds, and books. You can search by date released, by keywords, and even by format.

Zeroing In *(cont.)*

It's time to finalize your choice for a topic. Write it here:

Now that you have chosen a topic to research and present to the class, it's time to answer an important question about that topic: How does it affect the world around you? Some topics are very important to you and your school but have very little impact on the world as a whole. Other topics affect your whole state or country.

Directions: Look at the graphic below. The various rings represent the scope of those who are affected by your topic. Shade or color in each ring to show exactly what your topic affects. You may end up coloring just one ring or all of them.

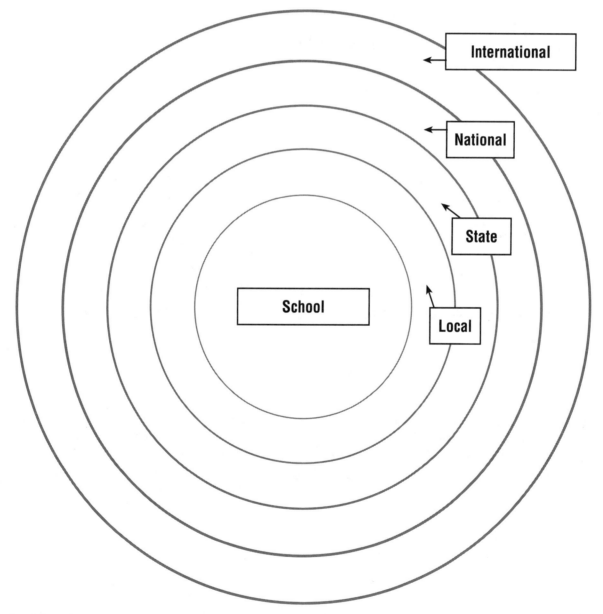

Write a Thesis Statement

For this project, you will be writing an essay that attempts to persuade your readers to see your side of the topic you have chosen. And in this essay, the most important sentence may very well be the thesis statement.

That's because the thesis statement is a map of your entire research essay. It not only tells the reader — in one sentence — what you believe, it also tells your audience the order in which your essay's elements will be found. In that way, it acts like a table of contents for your essay.

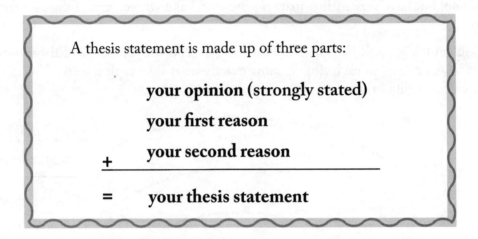

So, if you were to write a paper on why you should be able to drink water in class, the thesis statement might read as follows, depending on the stance for which you are choosing to advocate:

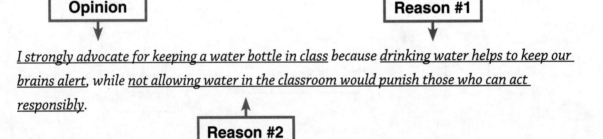

Now, looking at the sentence above, the reader knows that the first body paragraph of the essay will be on keeping students alert during the day and the second body paragraph will be on punishing the wrong people. Readers will know this because that is the order in which the reasons appear in the thesis statement. See, that's how the thesis statement is like a map or table of contents for your essay.

Write a Thesis Statement *(cont.)*

Directions: Look at the thesis statement below. It is from an essay disputing the need to pay students for their grades. On the thesis statement, do the following:

- ❑ Underline the phrase that states the author's opinion.
- ❑ Circle the phrase that indicates what the 1st body paragraph will be about.
- ❑ Draw a box around the phrase that indicates what the 2nd body paragraph will be about.

> **Thesis Statement**
>
> *We should definitely not pay students for grades because it does not teach a student to be motivated from the inside and districts cannot afford to pay the money in such hard economic times.*

Directions: Construct a possible thesis statement for a persuasive essay about the topic you have chosen for your Advocacy Research Project.

Your opinion: _____

_____

What 1st paragraph will be about: _____

_____

_____

_____

What 2nd paragraph will be about: _____

_____

_____

Your thesis statement: _____

_____

_____

_____

The Newspaper Article

A newspaper or online article is the perfect way to introduce the facts about your topic, without the presence of bias or opinion. It can also be a perfect multi-genre project in itself: newspaper articles combine writing, photographs, graphs, interviews, etc. But before you can incorporate all of those elements into a final product, you need know how to write the actual article first.

A newspaper article has a specific structure. It typically has five components:

1. **Headline** — This is the title of your article. It quickly grabs the reader's attention and tells him or her what the article is about.

2. **Byline** — This names the author of the article.

3. **Lead Section** — These intro paragraphs tell the reader the most important beats of the story in one glance. The first paragraph contains a *hook* to grab the reader's attention, and the section continues with the "Five Ws and One H" (Who, What, When, Where, Why, and How) about the subject.

4. **Expansion** — These are the next few paragraphs that build on the first paragraph. This is where the reader can learn about what people have said about the topic. Perhaps there are details like quotes or data to back up the topic of the article.

5. **Related Information** — This includes additional information that might prove interesting to the reader but that isn't important to understanding the initial purpose of the article.

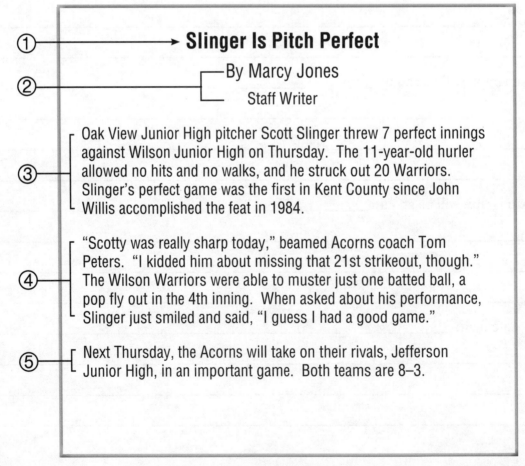

① **Slinger Is Pitch Perfect**

② By Marcy Jones
    Staff Writer

③ Oak View Junior High pitcher Scott Slinger threw 7 perfect innings against Wilson Junior High on Thursday. The 11-year-old hurler allowed no hits and no walks, and he struck out 20 Warriors. Slinger's perfect game was the first in Kent County since John Willis accomplished the feat in 1984.

④ "Scotty was really sharp today," beamed Acorns coach Tom Peters. "I kidded him about missing that 21st strikeout, though." The Wilson Warriors were able to muster just one batted ball, a pop fly out in the 4th inning. When asked about his performance, Slinger just smiled and said, "I guess I had a good game."

⑤ Next Thursday, the Acorns will take on their rivals, Jefferson Junior High, in an important game. Both teams are 8–3.

The Newspaper Article *(cont.)*

Directions: Go online and find a news article on an appropriate webpage. A good place to look would be *http://www.cnn.com/studentnews/*. Click on an article that you may be interested in. Cut and paste it into a word-processing document. Then do the following:

1. Use the features in your word-processing program to highlight certain elements of the article according to the color code below:

Who – blue	**Where** – yellow
What – green	**How** – pink
When – red	**Why** – orange

2. Then, underline the hook.

3. Next, read through the article again and **boldface** any quotes or other evidence that serves as details for the topic.

Directions: Once you have researched the topic you have chosen for your advocacy project, write an outline for a newspaper article on your topic. Include the headline and also the type of information you will include in the lead section and in the expansion section.

Rules to Remember

When thinking about your news article, remember these three rules of thumb for journalism:

1. **No bias.**

   Only stick to the facts; don't include your opinion for one side or the other. As a writer, pretend that you are the news anchor, just reporting the facts.

2. **Pick an angle and stick to it.**

   Decide the article's point of view and don't drift from it.

3. **Keep it simple and unemotional.**

   Many writing elements — like metaphors, similes, emotion, visualization, concrete description, or personal experience — are not suited to a news article.

Create a Graph

A *graph* is a visual display of data. To create a graph first takes collecting data and then converting that data stats into the visual interpretation.

For the purposes of your advocacy project, a graph can help you prove your point. You can begin by creating a question to ask of classmates, neighbors, community members, family, etc., and then you can collect the results. (Perhaps, for example, you want to know if people like *Star Wars* over *Star Trek*, or if students think letters are more important than numbers.) A graph can show your findings in a picture that is easily understood at a glance.

There are many frequently used formats for graphing, but the two most common are the bar graph and pie chart.

Bar Graphs

A *bar graph* uses rectangular bars to show the values of the things they represent. Bar graphs are great for showing the difference between values.

Directions: Look at the data given for a multi-genre project called "Traffic in Our Town." Use the results to fill in the bars on the graph below. The first bar has been done for you.

Students Polled: 36

Question: "How far do you travel to get to school?"

Results:

less than 1 mile = 6 students   3–5 miles = 9 students

1–3 miles = 15 students   6 or more miles = 6 students

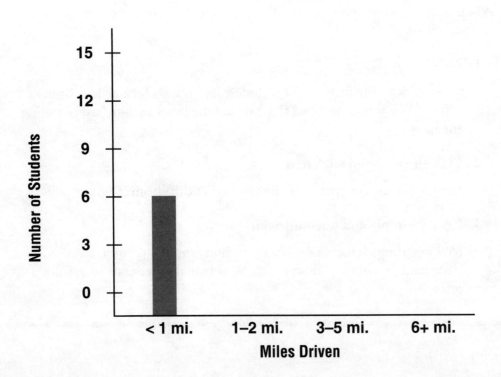

Create a Graph *(cont.)*

Pie Charts

A *pie chart* is a circular chart that is divided into sections based on the values of data. Pie charts are great for displaying the obvious differences when your data values are far apart.

Directions: Look at the data given for a multi-genre project called "Knowing Your Roots." Use the results to label the sections of the pie chart below. One section has been done for you.

Students Polled: 80

Question: "On which continent were your grandparents born?"

Results:

North America = 40

South America = 6

Asia = 20

Australia = 1

Europe = 10

Africa = 3

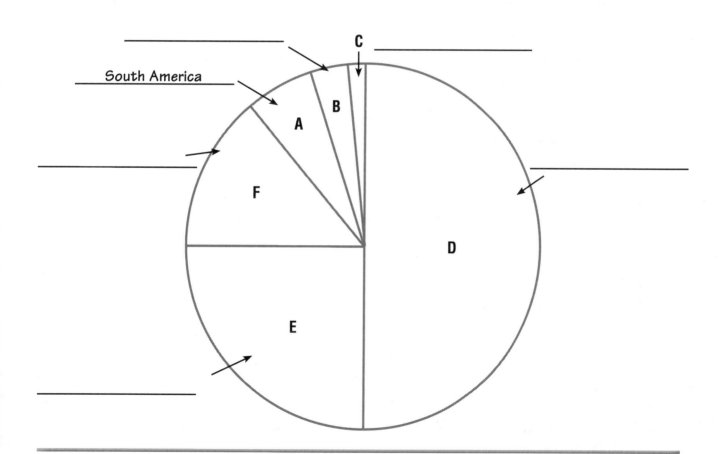

21st-Century Connection: Create your own poll using a website such as *polldaddy.com*. Insert the results into a spreadsheet program (for example, Excel) and create a quick visual 3-D bar graph or pie chart. Cut and paste the results into the typed final draft of a narrative or newspaper article.

A Call to Action

One of the most important parts of a persuasive essay is your proposed solution. You have to get your reader to want to do something as a result of learning about your issue.

A "call to action" does that. It calls a group of people together to act on solving a problem. There are many different ways to do this. Here are some methods:

❖ **Debate** — You can have each side present its case in the form of a civil argument.

❖ **Rock-Paper-Scissors** — You can choose two people to compete in a winner-take-all format.

❖ **Compromise** — Each side gives up a little, a middle ground is reached, and everyone "wins."

❖ **Petition** — You can influence an outcome by getting a lot of people to back you up.

❖ **Vote** — You can take a vote, and the majority opinion wins.

Directions: In the following activity, decide on which method you would like to ask your reader/audience to use in order to solve the problem. Include a reason why you would choose that method.

Statement of Opinion	Call to Action
1. Students should be able to sit with their friends in class.	Method: _____ Why?: _____ _____ _____
2. There should be a dog park built in the neighborhood.	Method: _____ Why?: _____ _____ _____
3. We need to save our public libraries!	Method: _____ Why?: _____ _____ _____

Unit Checklist

Below is a possible checklist for the "Advocacy Research" unit. It should help to organize your time and work as you move through the process of creating a full project. Look ahead on your checklist and never lose sight of deadlines!

Genre	Description	Due	Turned In
1. Persuasive Writing	Write a business letter to your teacher in order to pitch the project.		
2. Research	Complete Cornell notes. Include four separate sources, two of which can be Internet-based.		
3. Narrative	Write a short story on the topic.		
4. Bibliography	Include a works-cited page. Use the correct format.		
5. News Article	Write an article about your topic. Include a visual element (photo, graph, etc.).		
6. Poem	Write a poem in any format. Use figurative language and poetic devices.		
7. Your Choice	Choose an additional genre to depict your topic.		

Unit 3: Historical Advocacy Project

Teacher Instructions

Of course, you aren't limited to developing an advocacy project about current issues. Have students look through all of the events of history for debatable topics and interesting events. And like any project-based writing unit should, the "Historical Advocacy Project" allows students to choose the topic they wish to study and the format in which they want to present their results.

This unit includes the following components:

❖ **"A Historical Choice"** (page 89) — Explore ideas for historical topics. Several specific topics are suggested, along with an extensive list of important historical figures and events.

❖ **"Choose a Topic"** (page 90) — Hand out three copies of this worksheet to each student. Have students narrow down their choice of a historical advocacy topic to the three that most interest them. Students should then fill out a form for each of the three topics.

❖ **"Conduct an Interview"** (pages 91–93) — This section teaches students about the importance of interviewing those with knowledge about a subject. Provided are cheat sheets that give students valuable tips on how to prepare for and conduct a great interview. An activity page challenges students to read an excerpt from an interview and ask pertinent follow-up questions. Finally, each student is asked to compose an e-mail thanking a fictitious interview subject for his/her time and insights.

❖ **"The Political Cartoon"** (pages 94–95) — Use Benjamin Franklin's famous "Join, or Die" to introduce your students to political cartoons. Then have your students think about the symbols associated with their topics and create political cartoons of their own.

❖ **"Unit Checklist"** (page 96) — Help students stay focused, on task, and in front of deadlines.

Get started by following these steps:

Step 1 — Direct students to look for inspiration in textbooks or online at these resources:

❖ *http://www.animatedatlas.com/timeline.html*   ❖ *http://www.archives.gov/*
❖ *http://timelines.ws/*

There are so many choices that would work, and the topics chosen could even be tied into the curriculum currently being taught in your classroom. For instance, if your class is studying . . .

❖ ancient civilizations, a student could take a side in the Athens vs. Sparta debate.

❖ the Renaissance, a student could advocate for funding trips to the New World.

❖ American history, a student could debate whether Freedom for slaves should have been included in the Declaration of Independence.

Step 2 — Distribute the "A Historical Choice" page to your students and begin the process of picking historical advocacy topics.

A Historical Choice

What if you had lived sometime in the past and were witness to people or events that were so important they became a part of our history? If you could have taken a side and argued for a cause, which side would you have chosen?

It is time to use your imagination and your knowledge of what once was to argue from the point of view of someone who lived in a different time in history. Or, if you prefer, you can take the role of a historian looking back through time.

Here are some examples of topics based on historical people and events:

❏ Did Betsy Ross really sew the first American flag?

❏ Did George Washington ever smile?

❏ Why did Robert E. Lee order Gen. George Pickett to make his famous charge at Gettysburg?

❏ Was Meriwether Lewis (as in "Lewis and Clark") murdered, or did he commit suicide?

❏ Did Aaron Burr commit treason?

❏ Did Britain have the right to issue the Stamp Act against the colonists?

Those are just a few ideas. The possibilities are limitless! Below are some more people or concepts you could choose. Add a few of your own, then go back and check off the three people, events, or ideas that most interest you.

❏ Harriet Tubman

❏ John Adams

❏ Benjamin Franklin

❏ Capt. Blackbeard (Edward Teach)

❏ John Montagu, the 4th Earl of Sandwich (inventor of the sandwich)

❏ Dr. Joseph-Ignace Guillotin (inventor of the guillotine)

❏ the hot-air balloon

❏ the metric system

❏ the 1700 Cascadia earthquake

❏ _____

❏ _____

❏ _____

❏ _____

❏ _____

Once you have identified three debates or topics that you are interested in, fill out the "Choose a Topic" worksheet (page 90) to hone in on the topic you will eventually choose for your project.

Choose a Topic

Directions: After exploring your textbook or some online sites, fill out the following worksheet for each of three subjects that you might want to focus on. Think about topics that you will enjoy researching throughout the unit. Don't pick something that will bore you as soon as next week.

Topic → ⟨_____⟩

List three facts you already know about this topic:

1. _____

2. _____

3. _____

List three people from history associated with this topic:

1. _____

2. _____

3. _____

Next, answer the following questions about this topic:

1. Why is this person/issue/event important?_____

_____

2. Why are you interested in this topic?_____

_____

3. Why is this topic historically important?_____

_____

Finally, think about the resources you will need to research this topic. Where are you going to find your information?

Check off the resource(s) you believe you will use. Don't worry. You're not committed yet. In fact, as you research, you'll find your list of resources grows. One will lead you to another.

❑ Books   ❑ Websites   ❑ Podcasts

❑ Interviews   ❑ Videos

Conduct an Interview

One of the possible requirements of any research essay is an interview. Conducting *an* interview is easy; conducting a great interview is hard. The difference between the two is that the former is a dull Q & A, with you asking set questions and your subject answering with nice, neat responses. The latter — a great interview — is more like a cool conversation that flows naturally.

For a research project, you can interview an expert on the subject, a witness, an author, an educator, or anyone else who can give you some insight that you wouldn't be able to find out in a book or online. You want the subject to respond in a unique way you wouldn't find anywhere else.

To get a great interview takes planning. There are really two stages to conducting an interview: the preparation and the sit-down. There are tips to help you through both. Use the following cheat sheets to get the most out of your time with your subject.

Interviewing Tips
The Preparation

☞ Research your topic thoroughly.

☞ Research your interview subject and how he or she relates to your topic.

☞ Come prepared with a pen and paper, or better yet, a way to record the subject's voice.

☞ Come to the interview with a list of at least 10 questions. Make sure they are not "yes" or "no" questions.

☞ When you initially contact the person for an interview, don't assume that he or she has the time or the desire to meet you. Be polite and ask if he or she would be so kind as to give you some time.

☞ Arrive dressed for success.

☞ Be on time.

Interviewing Tips
The Actual Interview

☞ Use eye contact.

☞ Shake the interviewee's hand in greeting and when saying goodbye.

☞ Say, "Thank you."

☞ Ask a question that you've prepared, then listen to the response. A good rule of thumb would be to ask a follow-up question based on the response. This proves you are paying attention to the person's response and not just thinking about your next question.

☞ When the interview is over, go somewhere where you can write/type everything that you remember, even if you've recorded the interview. Note the person's clothes, the room, and the walls — everything that can serve to set a scene for those who read your interview.

Conduct an Interview (cont.)

In the following activity, you are going to practice asking questions based on an interviewee's answer. Let's pretend that you're interviewing a member of your local Board of Education. Here is a question you may ask at some point during the interview:

> "What are the checks and balances that are in place when running a school?"

The board member responds:

> "Well, not any one group or person can make the decisions without getting some approval or following a process. This way there can be input from multiple people who care about the issue. So, for instance, if we are deciding to start a new class or something, then we have a lot of different groups that need to help us make that decision and help us see ahead of time what will go into that decision."

Directions: Based on the board member's response, develop three questions you could ask to prove that you were listening to the response.

1. _____

   _____

   _____

   _____

2. _____

   _____

   _____

   _____

3. _____

   _____

   _____

   _____

Conduct an Interview *(cont.)*

After you have conducted an interview, you should definitely follow up your interview within a day with a more formal "thank you" to the person for granting you the interview.

Directions: Imagine that you have interviewed a professor at a local college on his/her knowledge of the American Revolution. Below are fields for an e-mail that you are sending to thank the professor for granting you the interview and giving you some of his/her time and insights into the subject.

Be sure to include these elements in the text:

❖ a greeting

❖ a reminder of the interview

❖ a mention of one of the professor's points that was particularly helpful

End the e-mail by thanking the professor again and signing off with your full name.

To:	
From:	
Subject:	

The Political Cartoon

A political cartoon is a visual way to comment on an issue or event. Cartooning has a rich history in newspapers and magazines, and it has been used to describe complex topics through simple drawings.

Political cartoons don't have to be funny. In fact, some of the best ones are serious.

Benjamin Franklin created one of the first recorded American political cartoons in 1754. It was a picture of a snake all cut up, and the caption read, "Join, or Die."

Courtesy of the Library of Congress, LC-USZC4-5315

Directions: Take a guess. Based on what you know about American history in the 18th century, what do you think the snake represents? What did Franklin mean in his caption?

_____

_____

_____

_____

_____

_____

_____

The Political Cartoon *(cont.)*

Directions: To create your own political cartoon, start by answering the following questions:

1. What is your topic? _____

2. What do you know about your topic? Create a list of what you already know.

   _____

   _____

   _____

3. What are symbols that can represent the key ideas of your topic?

   _____

   _____

   _____

4. What can the symbols be doing in your drawing to represent your topic?

   _____

   _____

   _____

Use the space below to create a rough draft of a political cartoon based on your subject.

Unit Checklist

Below is possible checklist for "Historical Advocacy" unit. It should help to organize your time and work as you move through the process of creating a full project. Look ahead on your checklist and never lose sight of deadlines!

Genre	Description	Due	Turned In
1. Persuasive Writing	Pitch your topic to your teacher for approval.		
2. Research	Write three pages of Cornell notes about your topic (one must be from an interview).		
3. Summary	Write a summary of your topic (the event, issue, person's impact on history).		
4. Bibliography	Include a works-cited page (use correct format).		
5. Container	Choose a container to display your project that reflects your topic.		
6. Oral Presentation	Write a first-person script as someone who lived during that time period. Allow for Q & A from the audience.		
7. Political Cartoon	Create a political cartoon that involves your topic.		
8. Your Choice	Choose an additional genre to depict your topic.		